SIMPSONS™ COMICS
GET SOME FANCY BOOK LEARNIN'

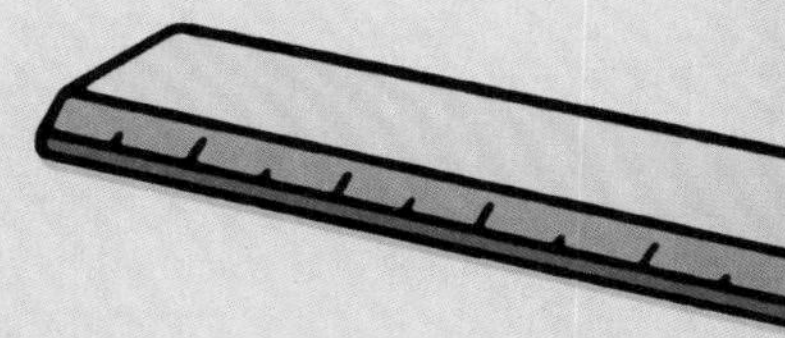

BONGO COMICS GROUP

SIMPSONS COMICS
GET SOME FANCY BOOK LEARNIN'

Collects Simpsons Comics 62, 70, 76, 126 and 148

Bongo Comics Group
P.O. Box 1963, Santa Monica, CA 90406-1963

FIRST EDITION

ISBN 978-1-892849-30-4

10 11 12 13 14 WCP 10 9 8 7 6 5 4 3 2 1

Publisher: Matt Groening
Creative Director: Bill Morrison
Managing Editor: Terry Delegeane
Director of Operations: Robert Zaugh
Art Director: Nathan Kane
Art Director Special Projects: Serban Cristescu
Production Manager: Christopher Ungar
Assistant Art Director: Chia-Hsien Jason Ho
Production/Design: Karen Bates, Nathan Hamill, Art Villanueva
Staff Artist: Mike Rote
Administration: Ruth Waytz, Pete Benson
Intern: Max Davison
Legal Guardian: Susan A. Grode

Trade Paperback Concepts and Design: Serban Cristescu

HarperCollins Editors: Hope Innelli, Jeremy Cesarec

Contributing Artists:
Karen Bates, John Costanza, Serban Cristescu, Dan Davis, Mike DeCarlo,
Luis Escobar, Jason Ho, Nathan Kane, Carol Lay, Joey Mason, Bill Morrison, Kevin M. Newman,
Phyllis Novin, Phil Ortiz, Howard Shum, Steve Steere Jr., Art Villanueva

Contributing Writers:
Ian Boothby, Carol Lay, Linda Medley, Sherri L. Smith

PRINTED IN CANADA

CONTENTS
5 GREEK TO ME
27 AESOP'S FABLES
32 PANDORA JR.
38 HUMPTY DUMPED
40 Hans Across America
67 1001 Arabian Nuts
93 BARD BOILED
121 Bible Stories

GREEK MYTHS

GREEK TO ME
NOT RERUNS AGAIN.
MATT GROENING PRESENTS
A MYTHICAL MILIEU OF MIRTH AND MADNESS BY
IAN BOOTHBY STORY
JOHN COSTANZA PENCILS
STEVE STEERE, JR. INKS
KAREN BATES LETTERS
ART VILLANUEVA COLORS
BILL MORRISON EDITOR

HOMER, WE DON'T WANT TO HEAR ABOUT "THE ILIAD" ANYMORE.
OKAY, NO PROBLEMO. ONCE UPON...
OR "THE ODYSSEY."

GIVE US A **GOOD** STORY, OR WE'LL TELL EVERYONE YOU'RE ***NOT REALLY BLIND***.
AAAAH! ***DON'T DO THAT!***

THE ONLY WAY I COULD GET THIS ***CUSHY STORYTELLING JOB*** IS BY ***PRETENDING*** TO BE BLIND.
OTHERWISE IT'S BACK TO BEING A ***SLAVE*** IN THE ***OLIVE MINES***.
THWAK!

I GOT THE IDEA OF ***FAKING*** BLIND-NESS FROM MY PAL OEDIPUS.
YOU WOULDN'T BELIEVE THE STORY ***I*** HAD TO MAKE UP.

OKAY, HERE'S A ***NEW ONE*** FOR YOU. ONCE THERE WERE THESE ***THREE ROOMMATES,*** ONE NAMED JACK, ONE NAMED JANET, AND ONE NAMED CHRISSY. BUT WHAT THEIR ***LAND-LORD*** MR. ROPER DIDN'T KNOW WAS...
TELL US A STORY ABOUT ***THE GODS***.

THE GODS, EH?
OKAY...

THE
GODS
IN
LABOR
PAINS

ONCE UPON A TIME THERE WAS A KING OF THE GODS NAMED ZEUS WHO WAS LOVED BY ONE AND ALL.
Mount Olympus
A GATED COMMUNITY

ZEUS!
AHHHH!
LIGHTING BOLTS

OOPS! MY LIGHTNING BOLTS FELL TO EARTH! WELL, THERE GOES SODOM AND GOMORRAH.
I'LL GET THE NEW GUY TO TAKE THE HEAT FOR IT.
OH, GOD, IT BURNS!

ZEUS, DID YOU TURN INTO A SWAN LAST NIGHT AND GO TO THE SINGLES BAR?
NO!

THEN WHAT'S WITH ALL THE FEATHERS AND THAT EGG YOU LAID?
OKAY, OKAY! I DID A BIT OF HARMLESS FLIRTING. BUT YOU KNOW ME, HERA, IT NEVER GOES FARTHER THAN THAT.

HEY, DAD! IT'S ME, HERCULES, YOUR ILLEGITIMATE SON!
D'OH!
WAP!

HAVE YOU NO SHAME?
I'M A DEMI-GOD AND PROUD OF IT, MAN.
NOW WHAT IS THERE TO DO AROUND THIS PLACE? THINK I'M GONNA CRASH FOR A WHILE.

OH, I'LL FIND YOU SOMETHING TO DO.

LATER THAT DAY...
TWELVE LABORS. AW, MAN! LABORS ARE WORSE THAN CHORES!
HEY, YOU THINK YOU GOT IT TOUGH? WHEN I WAS YOUR AGE, MY DAD ATE ME.

CAN I COME BACK HOME NOW?
NO! I CAN STILL SMELL ME ON YOUR BREATH.
CONSARN IT!

IT'S NOT FAIR. NONE OF THE OTHER KIDS HAVE TO FIGHT MONSTERS.

YO! LITTLE DUDE! I'M THE HYDRA AND I'M LIKE TOTALLY GOING TO ROB YOU OF YOUR GOLD AND EAT YOU.
AAAAH!

NO WAY, MAN!
SLICE!

YOU JUST DOUBLED YOUR TROUBLE, DUDE.
CUT OFF MY HEAD AND TWO MORE TAKE ITS PLACE!
NOW I'M TWICE AS ANGRY.

SLICE! SLICE!
SLICE! SLICE!

OKAY, I'M GONNA STOP DOING THAT NOW.
ANY LAST WORDS?

YEAH, WHICH ONE OF YOU IS GONNA GET MY MONEY?

I WILL.
NO ME!
I'LL KILL YOU!
I'LL *TOTALLY* KILL YOU FIRST!
IN YOUR DREAMS, DUDE.

BITE!
WHAM!
LIKE, OW!
GNASH!
DEFEATING THE HYDRA, OFF MY LIST...

LATER...
NOW TO CLEAN UP THE ***AUGEAN STABLES***.
P-U! CHOKE! COUGH!

LOOK AT THAT PATHETIC STABLE BOY. POINT AND LAUGH AT HIM FOR ME, WILL YOU, SERVANT?
HA, HA, HA, SIR!

YA-HOO! I'M ***RICH***!
WHAT?

EXPLAIN YOURSELF, BOY!
WELL, YOU KNOW, SINCE ***GOLD*** IS WORTHLESS, THIS ***DUNG MINE*** I'VE FOUND IS WORTH A ***FORTUNE***!

GOLD IS *WORTHLESS?*
I'VE BEEN OUT OF TOWN ON BUSINESS.
NO ONE TOLD YOU?

SORRY TO HEAR THAT. WELL, BACK TO MY FORTUNE!
WAIT! WOULD YOU BE WILLING TO *SELL* THIS DUNG MINE OF YOURS?

WHAT DO YOU GOT?
GOLD AND *LOTS* OF IT!
SURE I NEED A FEW *PAPER-WEIGHTS*. GO ON!
I'LL GIVE YOU MY HORSE, THE DEED TO MY HOME...

ARE YOU SURE THIS WAS A *GOOD DEAL,* SIR?
LESS TALK-ING AND MORE SHOVELING! WE NEED TO GET ALL THIS TO THE BANK BY MORNING!
LET'S SEE WHAT'S *NEXT* ON THE LIST.

HERMES, SEND THIS MESSAGE TO THE *GRECIAN SPCA*. I'VE LISTED SOME ANIMALS RUNNING AROUND WITH-OUT A LICENSE AND POSSIBLY RABID. THEY SHOULD PICK THEM UP.
A HIND, SOME LIONS, A BOAR, SOME BIRDS, A BULL, A COUPLE OF MARES, A DRAGON, SOME CATTLE, AND A THREE-HEADED DOG.

LATER...
WELL, THAT TOOK A WHILE, BUT THEY'RE ALL CAUGHT.
DADDY! I WANT TO ADOPT THE MINOTAUR.
NOW REMEMBER THIS CAN'T BE LIKE THE GRYPHON OR THE SPHINX. YOU HAVE TO FEED IT AND CHANGE THE LITTER BOX EVERY DAY.

YOU ONLY DID TEN OUT OF THE TWELVE LABORS!
LISTEN LADY, TEN OUT OF TWELVE IS A B+ AND THAT'S THE BEST GRADE I EVER GOT!

HRMMM...
HEY, WHAT'S WRONG?

OH, IT'S ZEUS! HE'S AT THE BAR AGAIN, AND I HAVE TO DO EVERYTHING.
YOU LOOK GOOD IN THAT CHAIR. MAYBE YOU SHOULD BE THE ONE RUNNING THINGS.
ME? NO, I...YOU THINK?

AND SO HERA TOOK OVER OLYMPUS, AND EVERYTHING WORKED OUT JUST FINE.

WELL, ALMOST EVERYTHING.
CLEAN YOUR ROOM!
DO YOUR HOMEWORK!
I SAID THERE'S A 9 P.M. CURFEW, AND I MEANT IT!
WAY TO GO JERK-ULES!

"THE HADES YOU SAY"
THE CASE YOU ARE ABOUT TO SEE IS REAL. THE LITIGANTS ARE NOT MORTALS. THEY ARE ACTUAL GODS WHO HAVE AGREED TO HAVE THEIR DISPUTE SETTLED HERE IN OUR FORUM...

...ATHENA'S COURT.
YOU MAY BE SEATED.
I HAVE GOAT LEGS.
ATHENA

I'VE READ YOUR COMPLAINTS. PERSEPHONE, YOU CLAIM THAT HADES KIDNAPPED YOU.
YES, YOUR HONOR.
OH, HERE WE GO!

MR. HADES, I AM JUST GOING TO SAY THIS ONCE. FIRST, TALK ONLY WHEN I AM ASKING A QUESTION, AND SECOND...
ATHENA

...PUT YOUR SHIRT BACK ON AND TAKE YOUR FEET OFF THE PODIUM.
OKAY! OKAY!
SHEEESH! WHAT IS THIS, CHURCH?
DEFENDANT

MR. HADES, WHAT IS YOUR SIDE OF THE STORY?
WELL, YOU SEE YOUR HONOR...

"IT ALL STARTED LIKE ANY OTHER DAY."
AND STAY OFF!
HADES
IF YOU WERE DEAD YOU'D BE HOME BY NOW.

WHASSA MATTER, HADES? YOU LOOK DEPRESSED.
THAT GUY HAS GOT TO LEARN TO PAY HIS TAB!
HUH? YOU SAY SOMETHING, CHARON?

I'M LONELY.
YOU GOT IT ALL! POWER! LOOKS! CORPSES COMING OUT THE WAZOO...!

WHY DON'T YA GET YOURSELF A WIFE?
THAT SOUNDS LIKE A JIM-DANDY IDEA.

SHUT UP, SISYPHUS!
WELL, I JUST DROPPED BY TO TELL YOU THAT IT TOOK FOREVER, BUT I FINALLY GOT THAT ROCK UP TO THE TOP OF THE HILL LIKE YOU WANTED.

AW, FIDDLESTICKS!
HEH, HEH!

MAYBE YOU'RE RIGHT, CHARON. I'M GONNA TRY DATING.

"THEN, JUDGE, I SAW THIS REAL PRETTY WOMAN IN THE LAND OF THE LIVING AND THOUGHT I'D ASK HER OUT."
WHAT A NICE FLOWER!

CRAAAAACK!
RUMBLE!
AAAAAH!

YOU SEE! THIS IS EXACTLY WHY I DON'T LIKE EATING OUTDOORS!

IS ALL THIS TRUE, MS. PERSEPHONE?
MY FLUTE'S STUCK.

IT IS, YOUR HONOR. I TOLD HIM IN NO UNCERTAIN TERMS HOW I FELT.

OW! WHAT WAS THAT FOR?
I WAS JUST ASKING YOU OUT.

YOU'VE GOT A LOT TO LEARN ABOUT DATING.
AND I WANT YOU TO TEACH ME.

WELL, I REALLY SHOULDN'T, BUT...
LET'S HAVE DINNER. JUST DINNER.
OKAY.

THESE POMEGRANATES ARE REALLY GOOD.
WAIT UNTIL YOU TASTE ANTOINE'S PORK CHOPS.

AAAAH!
WHAT?

OH, THE DECAYING ZOMBIE THING.
DON'T WORRY, HE WASHED HIS HANDS IN THE RIVER STYX.

AAAAAH!
NOW LET'S HAVE A DRINK OF LETH WATER AND RELAX!
680 BC

WATER FROM THE LETH RIVER MAKES YOU LOSE YOUR MEMORY.
THAT'S RIDICULOUS. I'VE BEEN DRINKING LETH WATER SINCE...UM...

HADES?
THAT'S RIGHT. AND YOU ARE...?

I'M LEAVING!
WAIT! GIVE ME ANOTHER CHANCE! LET'S GO DANCING!
WELL...

OKAY I HAVE TO ADMIT, EVEN WITH THE DEAD AROUND, THIS ***IS*** ROMANTIC. AND YOU ***ARE*** PRETTY CUTE.
YEAH, BUT WE NEED TO PICK UP THE PACE.

SLAM DANCE!

AAAH!

THAT DOES IT!
BUT!
NO BUTS! YOU LET ME GO, OR I'M TAKING YOU TO ***COURT!***

AND HERE WE ARE.
I'LL BE BACK WITH MY ***VERDICT*** IN FIVE MINUTES.
WHAM!

WHILE WE WAIT, LET'S FIND OUT WHAT PEOPLE THINK ABOUT STUFF.

SHE'S GOT TO KICK THAT DOG TO THE CURB!

HE'S GUILTY. ANYONE CAN SEE THAT.

I JUST WANNA GIVE A SHOUT OUT TO MY CREW IN ASGARD!
YO, THOR! I'M ON TV!
MY ALL FATHER WENT TO MIDGARD AND ALL I GOT WAS THIS LOUSY T-SHIRT

I'VE REACHED A VERDICT.
THIS IS CLEARLY A CUT AND DRIED CASE OF KIDNAPPING.
I THINK I HAVE FLEAS.

HA!

BUT THIS IS GOD-LAW. AND IF IT WASN'T FOR DISGUISES, SHAPESHIFTING, AND KIDNAPPING, THERE'D BE NEXT TO NO GOD-DATING AT ALL. HADES IS THEREFORE CLEARED OF ALL CHARGES.

HOWEVER, YOU, PERSEPHONE, OWE HADES FOR THE POMEGRANATES YOU ATE.
SORRY, BUT OUR DUMB LAWS ARE STILL THE LAW.

HOW ABOUT YOU?

I'LL SHOW YOU ALL! EVERY YEAR FROM NOW ON YOU'LL SUFFER BITTER COLD AND SNOW!

THEN WE'LL SEE WHO'S ***LAUGHING***.

LATER THAT YEAR...

HURRY UP WITH THE SNOWMAN'S HEAD!

HA! HA!

HOO HA!

AW, FIDDLE-DIDDLY STICKS!

WHEEEEE!

HA! HO! HO!

HA! HA!

HOORAY!

ROCK ON
MAN, IT SURE WAS HARD TO FIND THIS PLACE, BUT IT'S WORTH IT IF THE LEGENDS ARE **TRUE**.

UH...EXCUSE ME?
YES?

IS THIS THE PLACE WHERE A GUY CAN GO TO GET **STONED**?

YOU **COULD** SAY THAT.
COUGH! HACK!

HEH, HEH, HEH, HEH COUGH HEH, HEH!

ELSEWHERE...
PERSEUS! BE CAREFUL RIDING THAT MINI-CHARIOT TO SCHOOL.
I WISH THAT THE REGULAR CHARIOT DRIVER, OTTOVIUS, HADN'T DISAPPEARED MYSTERIOUSLY.
I'LL BE CAREFUL!

GO HAMSTERS, GO!
CRACK!

HEY, WATCH IT!
HEY!
WHOA!
YOW!

EAT MY DUST, SUCKERS!

WHAM!

YOU STRUCK THE KING!
I DIDN'T DO IT!

I SENTENCE YOU TO ***ONE HUNDRED YEARS DETENTION***!
UH...A WORD, MY LIEGE?

MAYBE HE COULD ***HELP*** YOU WITH YOUR ***OTHER*** PROBLEM.
AH, YES. SPLENDID IDEA. EITHER WAY, IT'S ***WIN-WIN***.

LISTEN YOUNG MAN, WE'LL FORGET THIS EVER HAPPENED IF YOU'LL ***PERFORM*** ONE ***SIMPLE ACT*** OF ***COMMUNITY SERVICE***.
WHAT? PICK UP LITTER? CLEAN UP GRAFFITI?

BRING ME ***THE HEAD OF MEDUSA***!

LATER...
THERE SHE IS.
RATS, SHE'S GOT COMPANY.
I'M JUST SAYING THAT ALL THE MEN I DATE ARE ***PIGS***.
WELL, ***CIRCE***, MAYBE THAT'S BECAUSE YOU TURN THEM ALL ***INTO*** PIGS.
HEH, HEH, HEH :COUGH: HEH, HEH!

WELL, I GOTTA GO. I HAVE A **HOT DATE** TONIGHT.
HOPE IT WORKS OUT.
IF NOT, IT'S A **BLT** FOR BREAKFAST.

OKAY, PERSEUS, SHE'S ALONE. HOW **HARD** CAN IT BE TO CUT OFF SOMEONE'S HEAD? DRUNK BARBERS DO IT EVERY DAY.

I SEE YOU.

HA! I CAME PREPARED! I HAVE **A MIRROR!**
IT'S NOT MY **LOOK** THAT TURNS MEN TO STONE. IT'S MY **SECOND-HAND SMOKE!**

UM...I'M GONNA START RUNNING NOW.
I UNDER-STAND.

HISSSSSS!
AAAH!

GOTTA TRY PLAN B.
HAMSTERS **AWAY**!

YUM!
AW, C'MON GUYS, I JUST FED YOU!
MMMM!

AAAAA

LATER...
YOU'RE **ALIVE**?!?!
YES, AND I'VE **HONORED** MY SIDE OF OUR DEAL. I'VE BROUGHT THE HEAD OF MEDUSA.

GASP!

AND I'M THROWING IN THE BODY FOR **FREE**.
WHAT'S THE MEANING OF THIS?

MEDUSA TOLD ME THAT YOU TWO USED TO DATE UNTIL SHE DUMPED YOU.
HE'S NEVER REALLY **GOTTEN OVER** ME. THIS WAS JUST HIS WAY OF GETTING MY ATTENTION.

I'VE NEVER FORGOTTEN YOU OR STOPPED CARING, YOU CRUEL DICTATOR YOU.
THAT'S RIDICULOUS. I...
REALLY?

WILL YOU MARRY ME AND MAKE ME THE HAPPIEST DESPOT IN THE WORLD?
I WILL!

AND SO...
WHAT A WONDERFUL WEDDING. THE BRIDE LOOKS SO BEAUTIFUL.

AND HERE COMES THE GROOM.
YOU ALWAYS LOVED THE STRONG SILENT TYPE.

I COULDN'T BE HAPPIER. HE'S MY ROCK.
AND NOW IT'S TIME FOR MY WEDDING GIFT.

DOVES. HOW SWEET!
COO!
COO!
COO!
THEY WERE OUT OF DOVES, SO I GOT PIGEONS INSTEAD.

PERSEUS!
HEH, HEH!

AND SO, ALL THE HEROES, GODS, KINGS, AND GORGONS LIVED **HAPPILY EVER AFTER**. THE END!

HEY? WHERE'D EVERYBODY GO?

ARE **YOU** STILL HERE? WE STOPPED LISTENING TO **YOUR STORY** HOURS AGO.
THEN WHO ARE YOU...

AESOP?
SORRY, WE'RE FULL UP, SIR. BUT THERE'S SOME **STANDING ROOM TICKETS** LEFT FOR THE TEN O'CLOCK SHOW.
AND SO THE HARE LEARNED THAT EVEN THOUGH HE WAS **FASTER** THAN THE TORTOISE, SLOW AND STEADY WINS THE RACE.

LOUSY, NON-BLIND, STORYTELLING SLAVE TAKING MY BUSINESS!
I GUESS NO ONE **CARES** ABOUT THE GODS ANYMORE.
I.O.U.
TIPS
WHAM!
TELL ME ABOUT IT.

OH...AND BARKEEP? IF MY **WIFE** CALLS, I'M NOT HERE.
THE END

AESOP'S FABLES

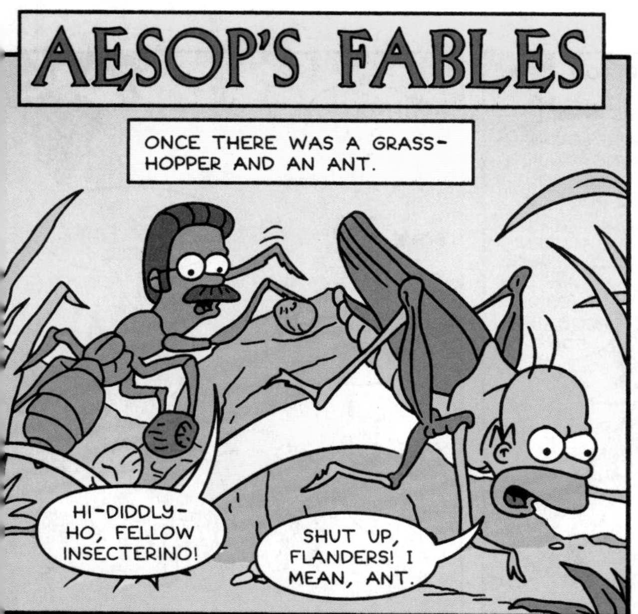

ONCE THERE WAS A GRASS-HOPPER AND AN ANT.
HI-DIDDLY-HO, FELLOW INSECTERINO!
SHUT UP, FLANDERS! I MEAN, ANT.

THE ANT WORKED HARD.

WHILE THE LAZY GRASS-HOPPER JUST DRANK BEER AND PLAYED HIS FIDDLE.

THE ANT SAID...
YOU REALLY SHOULD PREPARE FOR WINTER!
THE GRASSHOPPER REPLIED...
WHAT PART OF SHUT UP AREN'T YOUR ANTENNA RECEIVING?

THEN WINTER FINALLY CAME, AND THE ANT, WHO HAD WORKED HARD, HAD LOTS OF FOOD STORED, WHILE THE GRASSHOPPER HAD NONE.

HEY, ANT, CAN I HAVE HALF YOUR FOOD?
SURE.
THANKS.

GOSH-DIDDLY-DARN IT!
MORAL: WORKING IS FOR SUCKERS.

THERE ONCE WAS A FOX WHO SPOTTED SOME GRAPES.
YEAH! THAT'S WHAT I COULD GO FOR!

BUT THEY WERE TOO HIGH TO REACH.
GRRR! LOUSY STINKING GRAPES! I'LL GOUGE OUT YOUR PITS AND MAKE RAISINS OF YOUR CHILDREN!
AW, THEY'RE PROBABLY SOUR.

WOLF! WOLF!
HEY, I'M DOIN' A FABLE HERE!

A WOLF? WHERE?
OH, IT'S JUST A FOX!

HEY, NOW THAT YOU'RE HERE, HOW ABOUT GETTING ME THEM GRAPES?
YEAH, OKAY.

THESE AIN'T SOUR AT ALL. NOW HOW AM I GONNA MAKE WINE OUT OF 'EM?
IF YOU'RE NOT GOING TO EAT THOSE, CAN I HAVE THEM? THE ANT'S FOOD REALLY STINKS.
I CAN HEAR YOU, HOMER! I MEAN, GRASS-HOPPER!

WOLF! WOLF!

ACH! 'TIS JUST A WEE DOG.

WHAT'S WRONG?
I HAD A **WONDERFUL BONE,** BUT I SAW A DOG WITH ANOTHER ONE IN THE WATER, AND WHEN I TRIED TO BITE IT, I **LOST** MINE.

HOLY ZEUS! IT'S A **TALKING DOG!**
HEY, YOU'RE RIGHT. THAT **IS** PRETTY COOL.
SO? YOU'RE A TALKING FOX.

SPEAKING OF COOL, WHAT'S WITH THE **WEATHER,** MAN?

WE HAVE A **BET** GOING TO SEE WHO CAN MAKE YOU TAKE OFF YOUR JACKET **FIRST!**
COUGH! COUGH! WE HAVE TEN DRACHMAS RIDING ON IT.

I'LL TAKE IT OFF FOR WHOEVER GIVES ME **FIVE DRACHMAS** FIRST.

WIND IT IS!
NO FAIR! SHE **BLEW** MY FIVE AWAY!
WHAT ARE YOU GONNA DO WITH THE MONEY?

PUT IT ALL ON THE TORTOISE TO WIN THE BIG RACE!
Positively NO CHECKS
ARE YOU NUTS? THE ODDS ARE 300 TO 1!

AND THE WINNER IS... THE HARE!
SEE! I TOLD YA.
JUST WAIT.

MAY I HAVE YOUR ATTENTION PLEASE. AFTER A RANDOM URINE TEST FOR STEROIDS, THE HARE HAS BEEN DISQUALIFIED. THE TORTOISE WINS.
1
YES!

CONGRATULATIONS ON YER WIN, LAD!
YES, WELL DONE!
IT'S A WOLFMAN!

OH, NO, WE'RE NOT FALLING FOR THAT AGAIN!

NOT A WOLF, MAN. IT'S A WOLFMAN! AND THE MUMMY! AND DRACULA!

OH MY GODS! THEY'RE ATTACKING THE DANCING MONKEYS, THE JACKDAW, THE CRAB, AND IT'S MOTHER.

BUT HERE COME THE TWO FIGHTING COCKS AND THE EAGLE!
I'VE NE'ER SEEN SUCH AN INCREDIBLE BATTLE WITH SO MANY INTERESTING LOOKIN' CHARACTERS!

IT'D BE RIDICULOUS TO EVEN ASK ANY ARTIST TO TRY AND DRAW ALL THAT.

ZZZZAP! ZZZZAP!
AHHH! FLYING SAUCERS!
RUN FOR IT!

...AND THEN THE ALIENS FIRED THEIR DEATH RAYS, BUT WHAT THEY DIDN'T KNOW WAS THAT THE MOLE PEOPLE HAD PLANNED FOR THIS AND...
HOMER! WOULD YOU QUIT INTER-RUPTING MY FABLES?

I WAS JUST TRYING TO JAZZ THEM UP! YOU'RE NOT PLAYING WELL IN THE KEY 18-32 DEMOGRAPHIC.
HE'S RIGHT, YOU KNOW. I'M AFRAID WE'RE GOING TO HAVE TO GIVE YOUR SPOT TO AN INFOMERCIAL.

BUT...
NOW, NOW! YOU CAN'T HAVE A GREEK DEMOCRACY WITHOUT DEMOGRAPHICS.

HI, EVERY-BODY!
HI, HYPOCRATES!
HOW MUCH WOULD YOU PAY TO GET RID OF THAT ANNOYING SANDAL RASH?
MORAL? THE HADES IF I KNOW.

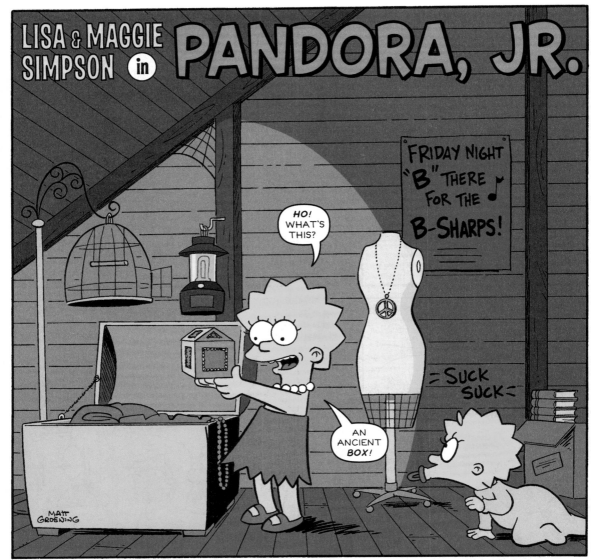

LISA & MAGGIE SIMPSON in PANDORA, JR.

FRIDAY NIGHT "B" THERE FOR THE B-SHARPS!

MATT GROENING

HO! WHAT'S THIS?

=SUCK SUCK=

AN ANCIENT *BOX!*

CAROL LAY
SCRIPT & ART

NATHAN KANE
COLORS

KAREN BATES
LETTERS

BILL MORRISON
EDITOR

THERE, THERE...I WAS JUST KIDDING. DON'T BE SCARED, MAGGIE.

HMM...I WONDER WHAT'S INSIDE?
SUCK SUCK

?

WAIT.
CURIOSITY IS GOOD. OTHERWISE, HOW WOULD WE LEARN AND INVENT THINGS?

BUT CURIOSITY CAN ALSO LEAD TO *TROUBLE*.
LET ME TELL YOU THE STORY OF "*PANDORA'S BOX*."

BACK IN ANCIENT TIMES, THE GOD ZEUS WAS MAD AT A MAN NAMED EPIMETHEUS FOR HELPING PROMETHEUS STEAL FIRE TO GIVE TO THE HUMANS. HE CREATED A BEAUTIFUL WIFE FOR EPIMETHEUS AND NAMED HER PANDORA.
YOU MAY KISS THE BRIDE.
"ZEUS WAS KIND OF MEAN, AND HE WANTED TO PLAY A TRICK ON HUMANITY."
HEH HEH HEH...

"SO HE GAVE PANDORA CURIOSITY, BUT HE ALSO GAVE HER AN ORNATE BOX AND SAID..."
YOU MUST NEVER OPEN THIS!

"THE GOOD WIFE STRUGGLED TO KEEP FROM OPENING THE BOX. AFTER ALL, THE BOSS OF THE GODS TOLD HER NEVER TO DO SO."

"BUT ONE DAY HER CURIOSITY WON OUT, AND SHE THOUGHT SHE MIGHT JUST TAKE A PEEK."
KREAKK...

"WHEN SHE DID SO, ALL KINDS OF DEMONS, DISEASE, AND SADNESS ESCAPED INTO THE WORLD."
"SHE TRIED TO SHUT THE BOX, BUT IT WAS TOO LATE."

"WHEN SHE LOOKED INSIDE, ALL THAT WAS LEFT WAS SMALL AND DELICATE."
"IT WAS **HOPE**."

SO SOMETIMES, LITTLE SISTER, SATISFYING CURIOSITY CAN LEAD TO MISERY.
SUCK SUCK

I HAVE AN IDEA! LET'S PRETEND I'M **ZEUS** AND YOU'RE **PANDORA**.

OK, PANDORA... DON'T OPEN THAT BOX.
EVER.
SUCK SUCK

LI-SA...!
COMING, MOM!

KREAK...
SUCK
SUCK
THE END

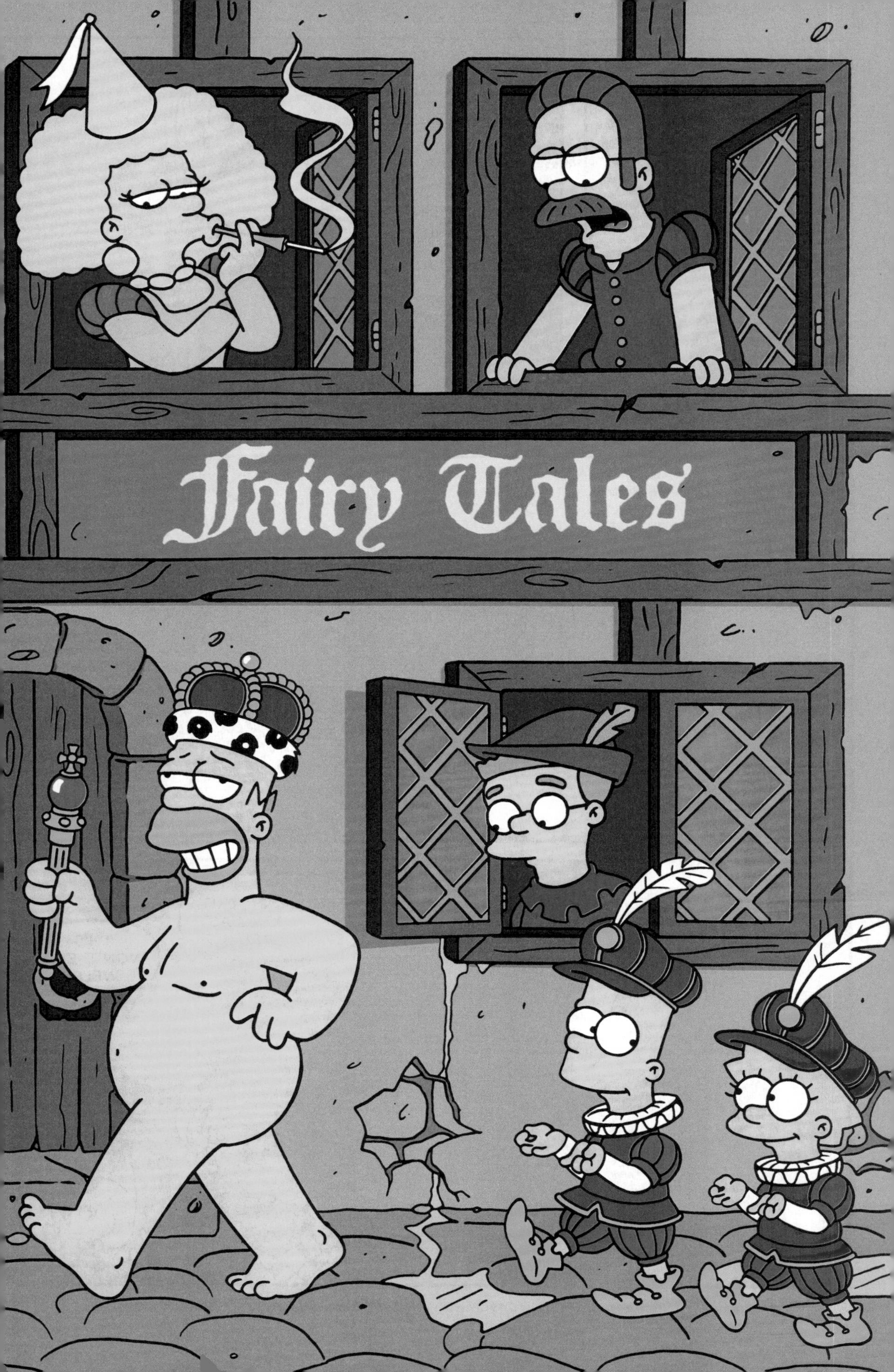
Fairy Tales

STORY: SHERRI SMITH • ART: JOHN COSTANZA / JASON HO • PRODUCTION: KAREN BATES / SERBAN CRISTESCU

HE'S CRAZY!
POOR LITTLE EGG BOY!
I CAN'T WATCH!
LADDERS ARE FUN! THEY'RE LIKE TINY STAIRS!
SIT TIGHT, SON, I'VE ALMOST GOT YOU!

I *CAN FLY*!
HUMPTY DUMPTY HAD A BIG FALL.

EWWW!
CRACK

ALL THE KING'S HORSES AND ALL THE KING'S MEN...
WHAT WILL WE TELL HIS PARENTS?
BRING THE *BACON*?
MY BRAIN IS YELLOW LIKE THE SUN.
...COULDN'T PUT HUMPTY TOGETHER AGAIN.

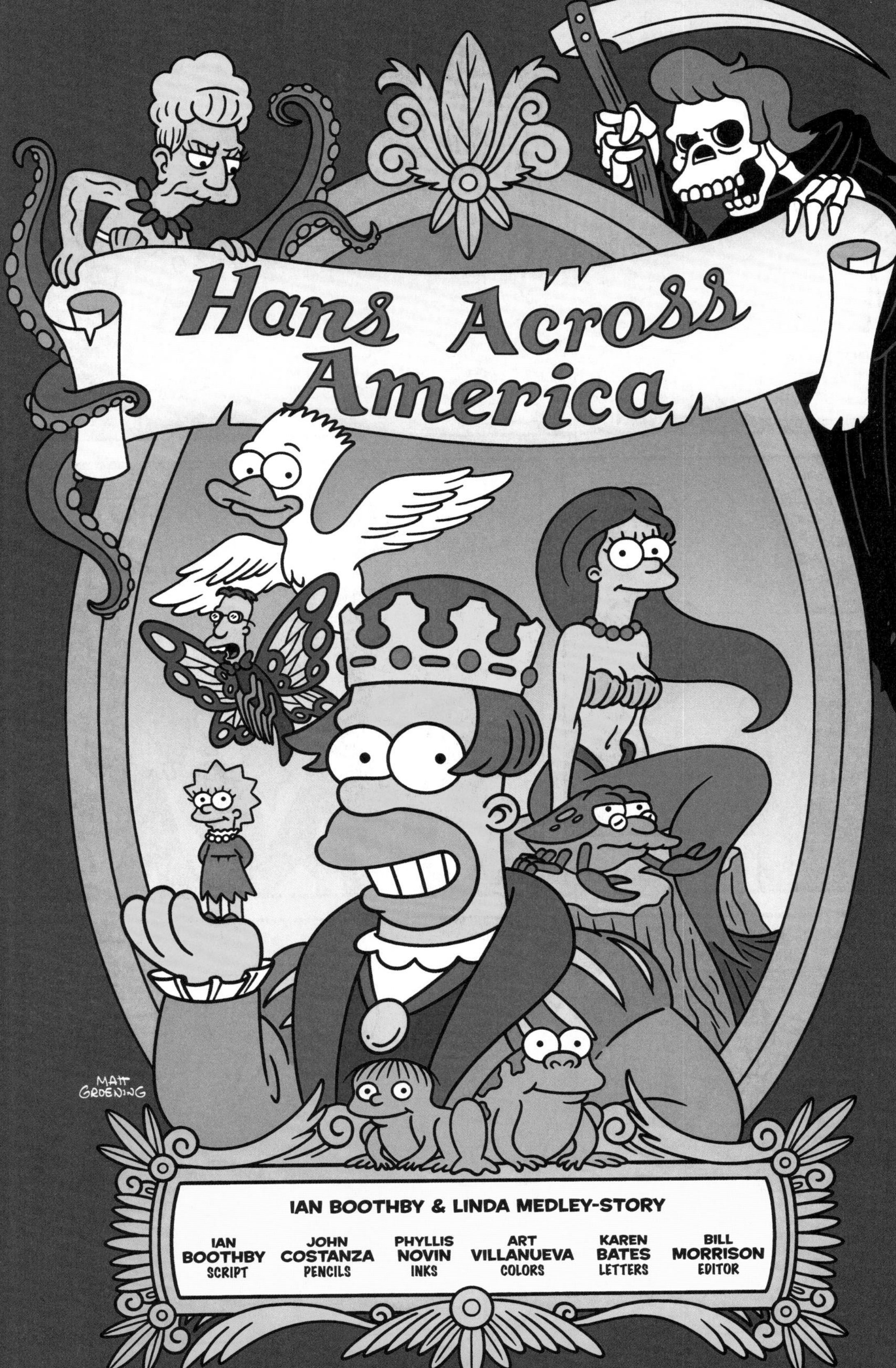

IAN BOOTHBY & LINDA MEDLEY-STORY

IAN BOOTHBY SCRIPT
JOHN COSTANZA PENCILS
PHYLLIS NOVIN INKS
ART VILLANUEVA COLORS
KAREN BATES LETTERS
BILL MORRISON EDITOR

HEY, MR. FLANDERS, ARE YOU HAVING A BARBEQUE?
I CAN BRING OVER SOME TOFU HOT DOGS IF YOU'D LIKE A MEAT-FREE ALTERATIVE!

DON'T WORRY, LISA. NO MEAT WILL BE FEELING *THIS* HEAT!
GLAD TO HEAR IT!

THIS FIRE'S FOR AN OLD-FASHIONED *BOOK BURNING!*
THE LITTLE MERMAID
WHAT?!

I ORDERED A SERIES OF CHRISTIAN FAIRY TALES ON THE INTERNET AND THEY SENT ME THESE *HANS CHRISTIAN ANDERSEN* ONES BY MISTAKE!

CAN'T RISK ROD AND TODD READING THEM SO...
WAIT! THOSE ARE *WONDERFUL* STORIES! LET ME READ A FEW TO YOUR SONS!

WELL, I DON'T KNOW. I HAVEN'T TRUSTED HANS CHRISTIAN ANDERSEN SINCE I TOOK THE BOYS TO THAT "LITTLE MERMAID" MOVIE WITH HER SKIMPY TOP AND THOSE SUGGESTIVE UNDERSEA TOWERS!
THE *REAL* STORY IS VERY DIFFERENT THAN THE MOVIE!

WELL, OKAY! BOYS, LISA'S GONNA READ YOU A STORY OR TWO!
YAY!

ONCE UPON A TIME, A MERMAID WAS HAVING HER EIGHTEENTH BIRTHDAY!
The Little Mermaid

YOU KNOW, I DON'T REALLY NEED CANDLES.
CLICK! CLICK!
GOOD, CAUSE THIS IS MURDER ON MY THUMB!

CONGRATS! YOU'RE NOW OLD ENOUGH TO SWIM TO THE SURFACE!
GASP! IS THAT SAFE?

SURE, WE DO IT ALL THE TIME!
IT'S REALLY HARD TO SMOKE UNDERWATER!

COME ON! WE'LL SHOW YOU!
THIS IS GONNA END BADLY!

WHY DO YOU ALWAYS HAVE TO BE SO NEGATIVE?
I'M A **HERMIT CRAB**. BEING AN ANTI-SOCIAL GRUMP IS WHAT I ***DO!***

IT'S SO BEAUTIFUL! THE SKY! THE CLOUDS!
COUGH! COUGH! YEAH!
INSPIRING *WHEEZE!*

IT'S ALL SO BEAUTIFUL! THE SKY! THE CLOUDS!
WHO'S *THAT?*
I DON'T KNOW, SOME KIND OF LAND APE. *COUGH!* DON'T WORRY, THEY'RE MORE SCARED OF ***YOU*** THAN YOU ARE OF ***THEM!***

WHOOOOOAH!
SPLASH!

I DON'T THINK HE CAN SWIM!
NOT OUR PROBLEM. *COUGH!* GET INVOLVED AND HE'LL PROBABLY END UP SUING YOU!

I HAVE TO DO SOMETHING!

SHORTLY...
HUH? WHERE AM I? WHAT'S WITH THE PALM LEAVES?

YOU WERE DROWNING AND NAKED, SO I MADE YOU THOSE!
NAKED? BUT LUIGI SAID HE MADE ME AN OUTFIT ONLY CLASSY PEOPLE COULD SEE!

SAY, THANKS FOR SAVING MY LIFE. WANNA GO OUT SOMETIME? A LITTLE DINNER AND DANCING?
DANCING? WELL, I...ER... THAT IS...

LOOK OVER THERE!
WHAT? WHO? WHERE? WHY?

HELLO?

LATER...
SO *THAT'S* MY PROBLEM. I NEED *LEGS* TO DANCE WITH THIS HANDSOME MAN!
CAN YOU HELP ME, SEA WITCH?

WHY DOES EVERYONE CALL ME "SEA WITCH"? MY NAME'S *AGNES!*
YOUR SON TOLD ME TO.
IT'S JUST A NICKNAME I HAVE FOR YOU, MOTHER. AN *AFFECTIONATE* NICKNAME!

HERE'S THE DEAL, TOOTS! I'LL GIVE YOU A PAIR OF GAMS, BUT I WANT YOUR TONGUE IN RETURN!
MY TONGUE?
YEAH, MINE'S NO GOOD. BURNED ALL MY TASTE BUDS OFF IN A HOT WING-EATING CONTEST!

LUCKILY, MERMAID TONGUES AND LOWER HALVES ARE DETACHABLE, SO THIS WAS PAINLESS...
MMMM...OH, AND ONE MORE THING I FORGOT TO TELL YOU.
IF YOUR TRUE LOVE MARRIES SOMEONE ELSE, YOU'LL TURN TO FOAM!

WHATSA MATTER, PRINCE HOMER?
I MET THE GIRL OF MY DREAMS TODAY, BUT SHE LEFT ME!

YOU'LL BOUNCE BACK. MAN, IF I WUZ A HANDSOME PRINCE LIKE YOU, I'D BE KISSING ALL THE PRINCESSES IN COMAS I COULD FIND, TRYING TO WAKE 'EM UP!
I DID THAT ONCE. I'M NOT ALLOWED AT THE HOSPITAL ANYMORE.

SQUEAK!

WOW, CHECK OUT THE LEGS ON HER!
THEY LOOK BRAND NEW!

GASP! IT'S YOU!

WAIT! WAIT! BEFORE YOU SAY ANYTHING, I HAVE TO GET THIS OFF MY CHEST!

I KNOW IT SOUNDS LIKE THE BEER, SCOTCH, ABSINTHE, AND GRAIN ALCOHOL TALKING, BUT I FELL IN LOVE WITH YOU TODAY!
WILL YOU DO ME THE HONOR OF BEING MY PRINCESS?

YOU ***WILL***?

YOU'VE MADE ME THE HAPPIEST PRINCE IN THE WORLD!

HEY!
NO, HE'S RIGHT. THEY CALL YOU THE HAPPY PRINCE, BUT YOU'RE REALLY A DOWNER!

AND SO...
WE ARE GATHERED HERE TODAY TO JOIN THIS COUPLE IN ROYAL WEDDED BLISS.
DO YOU TAKE PRINCE HOMER AS YOUR HUSBAND?

JUST SAY "I DO"!
COME ON, SWEETIE.

I HAVE TO HEAR AN "I DO"!

WELL?

FINE! DOES ANYONE WANT TO BE MY REBOUND BRIDE?

SURE, WHY NOT!

IF YOUR TRUE LOVE MARRIES SOMEONE ELSE, YOU'LL TURN TO FOAM!

LATER...
WHY SO GLUM, MY LIEGE? MARRIED LIFE NOT TREATING YOU WELL?
IT TURNS OUT WE HAD WHAT SHE CALLED "IRRECONCILABLE DIFFERENCES" AND HAD TO GET...WHAT'S THAT THING CALLED?

AN ANNULMENT?
IF THAT'S THE ONE WITH THE GUILLOTINE, THEN YEAH!

HAVE ANOTHER BEER!

WELL HELLO, HANDSOME!
HUH?

WHAT HAPPENED TO YOU?
IT'S A LONG STORY, BUT I STILL LOVE YOU! I JUST COULDN'T SAY IT BEFORE!

AND SO PRINCE HOMER MARRIED A MUG OF BEER BECAUSE HE WAS ROYALTY, AND THEY COULD DO WHATEVER THEY WANTED BACK THEN.
NOTHING IN THE BIBLE AGAINST IT, EITHER! I NOW PRONOUNCE YOU MAN AND ALE!

THE PRINCE AND THE PEA

THE PRINCE AND THE PEA
ONCE UPON A TIME THERE WAS A KNOCK AT A PALACE DOOR...
KNOCK KNOCK!
WHO COULD IT BE AT THIS HOUR?

OH HELLO, LOWLY SERVANT. I'M A PRINCE WHO WAS AT A COSTUME PARTY WHERE I WAS DRESSED AS A PEASANT. I HAD A FEW TOO MANY HOT MEAD TODDIES, WANDERED OFF, AND GOT LOST IN THE WOODS.
I NEED A PLACE TO STAY THE NIGHT.

WAIT A MINUTE, ASIDE FROM YOUR GOOD LOOKS, WHAT PROOF DO YOU HAVE THAT YOU'RE ROYALTY?
MY MEDICAL BRACELET SAYS I'M A HEMOPHILIAC. ALSO, I'M BARELY TOLERATING TALKING TO SOME-ONE AS POOR AS YOURSELF.

ALL RIGHT, I'LL SET UP YOUR BED CHAMBER!
THEN HOP TO IT, MAN!

THERE MUST BE SOME WAY TO DISCOVER IF HE'S REALLY A PRINCE.

HERE YOU GO, YOUR MAJESTY.

I HOPE YOU WILL ENJOY YOUR...
STOP YOUR TOWER OF BABBLING AND TELL ME THE MEANING OF THIS!

AS A MEMBER OF HIGH SOCIETY, I ASSUMED YOU'D WANT TO SLEEP AS FAR AWAY FROM IS COMMON FOLK ON THE GROUND AS POSSIBLE.
RIGHT YOU ARE!
NOW, UNLESS YOU EXPECT ME TO CLIMB THIS LADDER ON MY OWN...!

HERE YOU GO, YOUR MAJESTY. PLEASANT DREAMS!

NOW, IF HE FEELS THE SMALL PEA I PLACED UNDER THE BOTTOM MATTRESS, I'LL KNOW HE'S A TRUE PRINCE OF THE REALM.
KRUSTY BRAND
BED PEAS

THE NEXT DAY...
GOOD MORNING, YOUR HIGHNESS! HOW DID YOU SLEEP?

NOT A WINK! SOME SCALAWAG MUST HAVE PEA-ED THE BED!
YOU **ARE** A PRINCE!

WELL, OF COURSE I AM. *YAWN*!

NOW, I DEMAND BREAKFAST! QUAIL EGGS! DUCK BACON! GOOSE TOAST!

MY COMPLIMENTS! THIS CARPET IS SO SOFT, IT FEELS LIKE I'M WALKING ON AIR!

THUD
SNAP
CRACK

AND SO...
WHAT ARE ***YOU*** IN FOR? I THREW A TOMATO AT THE KING.
I STABBED A DUKE WITH A CARROT!
I KILLED A HANDSOME PRINCE WITH A PEA. I GOT LIFE IN PRISON FOR ***VEGICIDE REGICIDE!***
AND PARENTS STILL TELL THEIR KIDS VEGETABLES ARE GOOD FOR THEM. WHEN WILL THEY LEARN?

THE UGLY DUCKLING

SOB! SOB!
WHAT'S WRONG?

NO ONE LOVES ME BECAUSE I'M SO UGLY!
LOOKS AREN'T EVERY-THING!

WELL SURE, *YOU'D* SAY THAT. YOU'RE EVEN UGLIER THAN *ME!*
NUH-UH.

MOM, CAN HE LIVE WITH US?
AS LONG AS HE BEHAVES HIMSELF, HAS GOOD MANNERS, AND DOES HIS CHORES!

I GOTTA BE HONEST, LADY. PROBABLY NONE OF THAT'S GONNA HAPPEN.
OH WELL, IT'S NOT LIKE I HAVEN'T COMPROMISED BEFORE!
BRAAAAP!

LATER...
WOW! THANKS FOR MAKING ME A PART OF YOUR FAMILY! I'M REALLY HAPPY!
YOU'RE HAPPY BECAUSE YOU FOUND OUT BEAUTY IS JUST SKIN DEEP AND THE IMPORTANT THING IS TO BE YOURSELF?

NO, I'M HAPPY BECAUSE IT'S DUCK SEASON, NOT SWAN SEASON!
YEE-HAW HAW!
DUCK SEASON
BLAM
BAM

ONCE UPON A TIME, THERE WAS A VERY LAZY MAN.
CAN YOU HELP ME REACH THAT BOOK?
THE SNOW QUEEN
THE SNOW QUEEN
THE SHADOW

I WOULD ADVISE YOU TO FIRST PURCHASE A LADDER FROM THE HARDWARE STORE DOWN THE STREET.
WHEN I REACH UPWARDS, MY SHIRT RISES UP AND MY EXPOSED BELLY BECOMES THE SUBJECT OF TITTERING.

WELL THEN, I'LL JUST BUY MY BOOK ***SOMEWHERE ELSE***.
I THINK YOU WILL FIND I AM THE ***ONLY*** BOOKSELLER IN THIS PATHETIC ONE PRINTING PRESS TOWN. THERE ***IS*** NO REPLACEMENT FOR ME!

HEY, IT'S SUNSET. HOW COME YOU DON'T HAVE A SHADOW LIKE EVERYTHING ELSE?
WHAT? THAT'S RIDICULOUS! IT'S BARELY WORTH TURNING MY HEAD TO CONFIRM YOUR FOOLISHNESS!

GASP! THE LAD SPEAKS ***TRUE!***

WELL THE RESULTS FROM YOUR LEECH BLOODLETTING CAME BACK AND AS USUAL IT WAS POINTLESS. AS FOR YOUR PROBLEM, I'VE NEVER SEEN ANYTHING LIKE IT. MOST SHADOWS DON'T HAVE ANY MASS AT ALL.
BUT YOU BEING SO HEAVY, IT MUST HAVE ACTUALLY STARTED TO WEIGH ENOUGH TO BREAK FREE!

YOU MEAN...?
I'M SORRY... YES. YOU'LL NEVER MAKE SHADOW PUPPETS AGAIN.

The Tinder Box Emporium
OH WELL, I NEVER REALLY USED MY SHADOW ANYWAY.

HERE'S THAT BOOK YOU WANTED!
THANKS!

WHAT ARE YOU DOING IN MY STORE?
REPLACING YOU, OF COURSE.

BUT YOU'RE JUST A ***SHADOW***!
I'VE BEEN ATTACHED TO YOU YOUR WHOLE LIFE. ONCE YOU HAD HOPES, DREAMS, AND A WAISTLINE. NOW LOOK AT YOU! YOU'RE A SHADOW OF YOUR FORMER SELF!

I'M TAKING OVER YOUR LIFE, SINCE YOU'RE NOT USING IT!

NOW EITHER BUY SOMETHING, OR GET OUT! THIS ISN'T A LIBRARY!

THIS WILL NOT STAND! I CHALLENGE YOU TO A FIGHT! THE WINNER GETS MY LIFE!

OH, YOU WANT TO SHADOW BOX, DO YOU? FAIR ENOUGH!

WHIFF!

ARE YOU DONE?
GASP! WHEEZE!

PLEASE. THIS STORE IS ALL I HAVE. LET ME WORK HERE AT LEAST.
WELL, THERE IS ONE JOB AVAILABLE.

NEW NOVEL COMING SOON: THE RED SHOES
OH, PIPE DOWN! SHADOWS DON'T TALK! AND REMEMBER, COME LATE AFTERNOON, I WANT TO SEE YOU GETTING LONGER!
MOAN!

THUMBELINA

THUMBELINA
SO, DOC, IS IT A BOY OR A GIRL?
IT'S A HEALTHY, HAPPY LITTLE GIRL!

WHERE?
YOU HAVE TO SQUINT A BIT. IT IS AN ABNORMALLY SMALL BIRTH WEIGHT. DID ANYONE SMOKE AROUND THE MOTHER?

ER...
NOT THAT WE REMEMBER...

AND AFTER A FEW YEARS...
MMMM... THESE ARE GREAT BOAR CHOPS!
MAY I HAVE SOME MORE SALAD?

HOW WAS SCHOOL TODAY?
WHATEVER YOU HEARD, I CAN EXPLAIN!
I GOT ALL A'S ON MY REPORT CARD!

DOES ANYONE ELSE HEAR AN ANNOYING SQUEAKING SOUND?
THAT'S ME! HELLO! DOWN HERE!

FINE! IF *THAT'S* THE WAY THINGS ARE, I'LL RUN AWAY UNTIL I FIND A WAY TO GET THEM TO *NOTICE* ME!
I'M SURE I'LL BE FINE. WHAT'S THE WORST THAT COULD HAPPEN?

THWACK!

SIGH!
HEY, IT'S RUDE FOR FOOD TO SIGH WHEN MY MOUTH IS FULL!

CAN I CONVINCE YOU TO NOT EAT ME?
MAYBE. I'M LOOKING FOR A WIFE FOR MY SON!

MY BREATH SMELLS LIKE FLIES!
OKAY, ON SECOND THOUGHT, I'M GOOD WITH BEING EATEN!

GRAB HOLD OF MY THORAX, IF YOU WANT TO LIVE GA-HEY!

HERE YOU GO, MY LIEGE!
GREETINGS!
AND YOU ARE...?

THE KING OF THE FAIRIES!

OOOOOKAY!
IT'S NICE TO MEET SOMEONE WHO **NOTICES** ME, BUT DOESN'T WANT TO **EAT** ME!

OH, I NOTICE EVERYONE AND EVERY-THING IN THESE WOODS. YOU'RE WELCOME TO STAY IN MY KINGDOM AS LONG AS YOU LIKE!
IS EVERYONE HERE AS KIND AS YOU?

WELL, NOT THE SPRITES, PIXIES, AND ELVES!
HEY, NICE WINGS! DID YOUR MOMMY MAKE THEM FOR YOU?

MY WAND! BUT I NEED THAT TO COAT THE PUSSYWILLOWS IN MORNING DEW!
HA HA!

YOU HAVE TO STAND UP FOR YOURSELF!
AND WHAT AM I SUPPOSED TO DO? TOSS FAIRY DUST IN THEIR EYES? IT'S MORE EXPENSIVE THAN YOU'D THINK!

COME ON! YOU CALL THIS GUY A CHALLENGE? JUST LOOK AT HIM!
UM...I CAN HEAR YOU!

I'M TRYING TO HELP YOU. PLAY ALONG!
I GUESS YOU'RE RIGHT. BULLYING HIM EVERY DAY IS GETTING' KINDA OLD!

WHAT IF I HAD A NEW JOB FOR YOU?
DOES IT INVOLVE SENSELESS VIOLENCE?

AND SO...
GREAT GRILLED GRINCH, HONEY!
WILL YOU PLEASE PASS THE BUTTER?

SLAP!
THE LADY SAID SHE WANTS THE BUTTER!

YESSIR, MR. SPRITE, SIR!
EXCELLENT!

THE GOOD MOTHER

MY HAIR?
BLARG!
HAND ME THE SCISSORS!

SHORTLY...
MY CHILDREN ARE WORTH ANY PRICE.

THANKS FOR THE ADDRESS!
PURRRRRR!

HE LIVES AT THE CORNER OF ELYSIAN AND TARTARUS. THAT'S DOESN'T SOUND TOO FAR AWAY.
PHONE BOOK OF THE DEAD

TWO YEARS LATER...
ALL RIGHT, THAT WAS FARTHER THAN IT SEEMED.
NOW WHAT? A RIVER? BUT I CAN'T SWIM!

SOB! BUT I'M SO CLOSE! OH, KIDS, I'M SO SORRY! I'VE FAILED YOU!

PLINK!
PLUNK!

DID YOU JUST CRY YOUR EYES OUT?

I SUPPOSE SO. WHO'S TALKING TO ME?
EEEEEEW! THAT IS SOOOOO GROSS!

HERE, TAKE THEM BACK!
PTTUUUUI!
BUT MY CHILDREN ARE STILL TRAPPED ON THE OTHER SIDE OF YOU!

JUST GO, AND DON'T DROP ANY MORE OF YOUR ORGANS IN ME!

DEATH'S DOOR NO SALESMEN
THIS MUST BE IT!

DEATH! AT LAST!
CAN THIS WAIT? I'M PACKING!
DEATH'S TAKING A HOLIDAY!
DEATH'S DOOR NO SALESMEN

I'M NOT LEAVING WITHOUT MY CHILDREN! UNLESS YOU WANT A BRUSH WITH DEATH, YOU'LL...
FINE! YOU WIN! THEY'RE, LIKE, OUT BACK!

YOU PLANTED THEM IN YOUR GARDEN?
IT WAS THE ONLY WAY TO STOP THEM RUNNING AROUND. AND THEY'RE GREAT FOR THE ROSES!
MOM!

NOW, BEFORE I GIVE THEM TO YOU, LET ME TELL YOU ONE SECRET THAT MIGHT CHANGE YOUR MIND ABOUT TAKING THEM BACK!
ONE OF YOUR CHILDREN WILL GROW UP BAD AND THE OTHER WILL GROW UP GOOD.

AND HERE'S A SECRET FOR YOU!
I'LL LOVE THEM BOTH THE SAME!

AND SO...
YOU HAVEN'T EVEN TOUCHED YOUR SALAD, LISA.
IT'S JUST THAT NOW THAT I'M A PLANT, IT FEELS WRONG TO EAT ANOTHER LEAFY CREATURE.

COULD YOU PASS THE PORK CHOPS?
THAT'S MY GIRL! YOU KIDS SHOULD GET KIDNAPPED BY DEATH MORE OFTEN!

SO YOU SEE, HANS CHRISTIAN ANDERSEN IS NOTHING TO BE AFRAID OF!

ROD? TODD?!

OH SORRY, LISA. ROD GOT SCARED WHEN THE MAN FELL OUT OF THE BOAT, AND WE'VE BEEN READING OUR OWN BOOK SINCE THEN.
VEGEMITE TALES

WHAT ARE YOU READING?
VEGEMITE TALES! THEY'RE MORAL STORIES TOLD USING AUSTRALIAN FOOD PRODUCTS!
VEGEMITE TALES

WANNA READ WITH US?
WHY NOT?
VEGEMITE TALES

LISTEN, SHRIMPY, YOU'D BETTER BE TELLING BRUCE YOU STOLE HIS BOOMERANG, OR WHEN YOU DIE, YOU'LL END UP IN THE **OTHER** LAND DOWN UNDER.
AND THAT'S **ONE BARBIE**, I DON'T WANT TO END UP ON! I'VE LEARNED **MY** LESSON, MATE!
SIGH!
THE END

ARABIAN

TALES

MATT GROENING presents

1001 ARABIAN NUTS

KING MOMAR SHAHRYAR WAS A GENTLE RULER, BELOVED BY ALL OF HIS PEOPLE FOR BEING KIND AND FOURGIVING...

IAN BOOTHBY SCRIPT · PHIL ORTIZ PENCILS · MIKE DECARLO INKS · ART VILLANUEVA COLORS · KAREN BATES LETTERS · BILL MORRISON EDITOR

YA SPELLED FORGIVING WRONG!
GUARDS! THROW HIM IN THE DUNGEON FOR LIFE!

YOUR BLIND DATE IS HERE, YOUR HIGH-NESS!
SHE IS? WELL, SEND HER IN!

HELLO.
AW NUTS! THEY WAS SUPPOSED TO BLIND YA!
SORRY ABOUT MY UGLY ROYAL MUG!

OH NO, I THINK YOUR FACE HAS A LOT OF CHARACTER.
REALLY? YOU'RE NOT JUST SAYING THAT? BECAUSE I CAN GET SOMEONE TO GOUGE OUT YOUR EYES. IT'S NO PROBLEM!

NO, THAT'S FINE! SO WHAT DO YOU WANT TO DO ON OUR DATE?
DINNER, A SHOW, THEN I'LL TRY TO PUT THE MOVES ON YOU, YOU'LL REJECT ME, AND I'LL HAVE YOU EXECUTED!

WHAT?
MY LAST FEW DATES DIDN'T END WELL!
HELEN
SELMA
EDNA
PATTY
AGNES
LUANNE
COOKIE

ARE YOU SURE YOU WANT TO GO OUT? YOU LOOK *TIRED*.
¦YAWN!¦ YEAH, I JUST CAN'T GET TO SLEEP AT NIGHT!

MAYBE HAVING MY BEDROOM RIGHT NEXT TO THE TORTURE CHAMBER WASN'T THE GREATEST IDEA. MAN, THOSE GUYS NEVER SHUT UP!

WHY DON'T I TELL YOU SOME STORIES TO HELP YOU SLEEP?

WHY NOT? AND IF I LIKE THEM, YOU CAN LIVE ANOTHER NIGHT!
SOUNDS GOOD TO ME!

ONCE UPON A TIME THERE WAS A POOR MAN WHO FOUND A MAGICAL LAMP!

ALA-DIDDLY-ADDIN AND HIS MAGIC LAMP
BLESS THIS TENT
DID YOU FIND ANY FOOD TODAY, DADDY?
SIGH! SORRY, BOYS! I WAS HUNTING FOR CHOW, BUT ALL I FOUND WAS THIS OLD LAMP!

OH WELL, NO USE WASTING TIME COMPLAININ'! MAYBE IF I SHINE IT UP, I CAN TRADE IT FOR A FEW CRUMBS OF BREAD!
RUB! RUB!

HOLY SMOKE!

AWWWWW!
POOF!

WHAT DO YOU WANT? I WAS ASLEEP IN THAT LAMP A THOUSAND YEARS, AND I WAS JUST STARTING TO GET COMFORTABLE!
SCRATCH SCRATCH

THE NAME'S ALADDIN! SO ARE YOU A REAL GENIE? DO I GET THREE WISHES?
WHOA WHOA WHOA, SLOW DOWN!

YEAH, YOU'VE GOT THREE WISHES. BUT WHY IS EVERY-THING ABOUT YOU?
LOOK AT ME! I HAVEN'T HAD A THING TO DRINK IN A THOUSAND YEARS!

THEN YOU SHOULD HAVE A DRINK!
WISH NUMBER ONE HAS BEEN GRANTED!
POOF!

HEY!
GENIE RULE NUMBER ONE! NO TAKE BACKS!

OKAY, THIS TIME I WISH MY FAMILY HAD ENOUGH TO EAT!
OKAY, CHECK THIS OUT! A LITTLE ABRACA-DAB'LL DO YA!

ALADDIN'S
ALL-YOU-CAN-EAT BUFFET AND 'GO-GO' BAR
BUFFET
GASP! AVERT YOUR EYES, BOYS!
DADDY?
WHY ARE THOSE LADIES IN CAGES IN THEIR UNDERWEAR?
WISH NUMBER TWO IS GRANTED! SO WHAT DO YOU THINK?

WHAT'S WITH ALL THE HARLOTS?
WELL, I NOTICED YOU WERE A SWING-ING SINGLE AND THOUGHT YOU MIGHT ENJOY--

I'M A **WIDOWER! MY WIFE** WAS THE ONLY WOMAN I'D EVER WANT TO SEE **IN A CAGE**.
WAIT, FORGET I SAID THAT!

WISH NUMBER THREE GRANTED! I'LL **FORGET** THIS CONVERSATION!
POOF!

THAT'S NOT FAIR. THAT WAS MY LAST WISH!
WHAT'S NOT FAIR? YOU'VE ONLY USED **TWO WISHES** AS FAR AS I REMEMBER!

OKAY, I HAVE IT! I WANT MY WIFE BACK!
WIFE BACK FROM THE DEAD? :PFFFT!: THAT'S TOO EASY!
LET'S MAKE IT INTERESTING. DO YOU WANT HER AS A BLONDE, A REDHEAD, OR MAYBE WITH :RRRROWL: BLUE HAIR!

NONE OF THAT! I WANT MY WIFE BACK JUST AS SHE IS!
WISH NUMBER THREE GRANTED!

ALADDIN!
OH, HONEY, IT'S SO GOOD TO HEAR YOUR VOICE I...

THERE YOU GO! ONE WIFE. AS IS!
I...I...I...!

WHAT IS IT? DO I LOOK FAT?
NO! NOT AT ALL!

WHAT'S ALL THIS? IS THIS HOW YOU'RE RAISING OUR CHILDREN?
NO! IT'S NOT WHAT IT LOOKS LIKE!
YOU'RE NOT EVEN WHAT YOU LOOK LIKE!

GENIE, I NEED ONE MORE WISH!
SORRY, GENIE RULES ARE GENIE RULES!

YOU CAN HAVE FIRST CRACK AT THE BUFFET!
THROW IN FIRST DIBS ON THE MAKE YOUR OWN SUNDAE BAR AND YOU'VE GOT YOURSELF A WISH!

MAKE MAUDE...TURN HER INTO... CHANGE HER BACK INTO...

AW NO!
THIS IS JUST GOING TO BE ONE OF YOUR TRICKS, YOU MEANIE GENIE!

I SAY I WANT HER BACK TO THE WAY SHE USED TO BE, AND YOU'LL JUST CHANGE HER INTO A BABY OR SOME-THING! AM I RIGHT?
HEH HEH! THAT WOULD BE A GOOD ONE!

I WISH YOU'D ESCORT YOURSELF OUT OF TOWN!

WISH GRANTED! YOU HEARD THE MAN! GET LOST!
HEY! WATCH IT! I BRUISE MYSELF EASILY!
POOF!

CAN I AT LEAST HAVE A DRINK BEFORE I GET KICKED OUT?
WELL, THAT DOES SOUND FAIR!

AND SO, SHORTLY...
ARE YOU REALLY OUR MOMMY?
SHE'D BE NEAT TO HAVE AROUND ON HALLOWEEN...IF WE CELEBRATED IT!
WAIT UNTIL MY MOTHER HEARS WHAT YOU WERE UP TO WHILE I WAS GONE!
YOU KNOW WHO'S A GREAT GUY? YOU!
NO, NO! SHUT UP! YOU'RE THE BEST!

YOUR MOTHER? BUT SHE'S DEAD!
AND I EXPECT YOU TO BRING HER BACK AS WELL!

YO, AL! YOUR OLD LADY SAID IT'D BE COOL IF WE CRASHED AT YOUR PLACE UNTIL WE'RE BACK ON OUR FEET!
YEAH, BUT GET THIS! WE DON'T HAVE FEET!

GRRRR!

OW!
OH, SURE'N YOU FOUND ME POT O' GOLD. NOW I HAVE TO GRANT YOUR GREATEST WISH!
CLANG!

BOOT!

APU BABA AND THE FOUR THIEVES

DISCOUNT OLIVES
MAN, CARRYING ALL THIS STUFF WAS EASIER WHEN WE HAD *FORTY* THIEVES.
WELL, THE OTHER THIRTY-SIX WANTED MEDICAL AND DENTAL, SO WE HAD TO LET THEM GO!

WHY, THOSE DIRTY THIEVING THIEVES! SO *THEY* ARE THE ONES WHO HAVE BEEN ROBBING MY STORE!

WANNA CHECK IF WE'RE BEING FOLLOWED?
NAH, I SLEPT ON A ROCK LAST NIGHT AND GOT A STIFF NECK. I'M GONNA STICK WITH LOOKING STRAIGHT AHEAD!

OPEN SESAME!

THE *ROCK!* IT IS *ROLLING!* OH, IF ONLY WE HAD SUCH A SECURITY SYSTEM AT THE STORE ...OR AT LEAST A FOURTH WALL.

LATER...
FINALLY! THEY ARE LEAVING! NOW IS MY CHANCE!

OPEN...UM... **SESAME?**

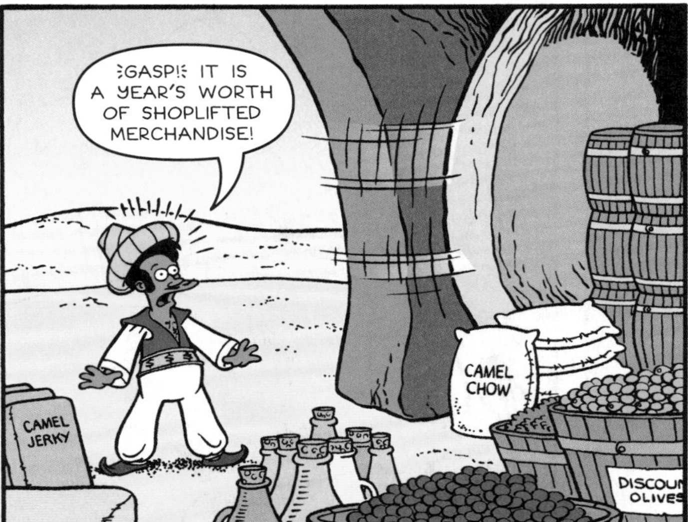
GASP! IT IS A YEAR'S WORTH OF SHOPLIFTED MERCHANDISE!
CAMEL CHOW
CAMEL JERKY
DISCOUN OLIVES

WELL, IT IS TIME TO GET YOU BACK ON MY SHELVES WHERE I CAN OVER-PRICE YOU!

WHAM!
CAM CHOW
DISCOUN OLIVE

WHO ARE **YOU**?
SESAME! YOU DON'T THINK THAT ROCK MOVES **ITSELF** DO YOU?

I SUPPOSE THE THING TO DO NOW IS TO LET ME TAKE MY MERCHANDISE, THEN WE CAN BOTH GO OUR SEPARATE WAYS AND FORGET ABOUT THIS WHOLE INCIDENT.

I WAS THINKING OF BEATING YOU TO A PULP! YOU CAN TRY AND FIGHT BACK, BUT I WARN YOU, I WAS GIVEN A BLESSING AS A CHILD.
NO OTHER PERSON CAN HURT ME!

THAT IS QUITE THE BLESSING! I WAS BLESSED WITH A BROTHER WHO ONCE TAUGHT ME THAT YOU CAN TELL IF A PERSON IS A GOOD FIGHTER IF THEIR FIST IS WIDER THAN THEIR FACE!

REALLY?
WHAT WAS THE OTHER THING HE USED TO SAY? OH YES...

QUIT HITTING YOURSELF!
POW!

OH MY, THIS WILL TAKE MANY, MANY TRIPS UNTIL I AM RESTOCKED!
DISCOUNT DATES

MANY, MANY TRIPS LATER...
OUR STUFF! SOMEONE SWIPED IT!
THIS IS GOING TO LOOK REALLY BAD AT OUR NEXT SHARE-HOLDERS MEETING!

I RECOGNIZE THOSE SANDAL PRINTS! IT'S APU BABA THE SHOP-KEEPER!

YOU RECOGNIZE *SANDAL PRINTS*?
I ADMIRE A GOOD PAIR OF SHOES! SO WHAT?

DUMMY UP, YOU TWO! I HAVE A PLAN!

HELLO, STRANGER! HOW MAY I SERVE YOU TODAY IN MY FULLY-STOCKED SHOP?
CAMEL CHOW
CAMEL JERKY
CAMEL JERKY

HELLO! I'M FROM THE SHEIK-E-MART HEAD OFFICE IN...WHEREVER THAT IS. I'VE GOT A NEW COLD DRINK DISPENSER THAT MAKES SOMETHING CALLED A *SQUISHEE*!
SQUISHEE MACHINE

I'LL SET IT UP FOR YOU. JUST FORGET IT'S EVEN HERE!
VERY WELL, IF YOU NEED ME I SHALL BE CHANGING THE EXPIRATION DATE ON THE CHICKPEAS!

HE'S FALLEN FOR IT. NOW ALL WE HAVE TO DO IS WAIT UNTIL HE GETS TIRED, AND WHEN HE LEAST EXPECTS IT, WE ALL JUMP HIM, BEAT HIM WITHIN AN INCH OF HIS LIFE, AND TAKE EVERY-THING BACK!
SCOUNT OLIVES

OH, MR. INSTALLER MAN, I...
NOW WHERE DID HE GO?

OH WELL, SINCE I HAVE NOTHING TO FEAR, I'LL JUST TURN MY BACK TO THE MACHINE AND TAKE A NAP.
UISHEE

AWESOME PLAN!
OKAY, I DON'T KNOW WHOSE HAND THAT IS ON MY BUTT, BUT IT BETTER BE THAT MINE'S JUST FALLEN ASLEEP!
ANY SECOND NOW!

BUT BEFORE I DO, I SHOULD FILL THE SQUISHEE MACHINE. OH NO! I DON'T HAVE ANY COLD WATER FOR THE COLD DRINKS!
SQUIS

I'M SURE THIS SCALDING HOT WATER WILL DO JUST FINE!
SSSSSSS!

AAAAAH!

OH MY! YOU THIEVES ARE IN **HOT WATER** NOW!

QUICKLY! JUMP INTO THESE VATS OF OLIVE OIL. OIL AND WATER DON'T MIX AND IT SHOULD SOOTHE YOUR BURNS!
OLIVE OIL
OLIVE OIL

BUT, HOPEFULLY, IT IS NOT OIL THAT HAS BEEN SITTING IN THE SUN. IT WOULD BE EVEN HOTTER THAN THE WATER!
AAAAH!

WE'RE GONNA TRASH YOU!
WHAT A MESS!
SESAME! CLEAN UP ON AISLE ONE!

SESAME?
SORRY, BOSS, BUT HE OFFERED BOTH MEDICAL AND DENTAL!

AAAAAH!
THANK YOU! DON'T COME AGAIN!
PUSH!

Y'KNOW, THAT WAS A REALLY GOOD PUSH!

WELL, THEY'RE GOING TO BE GOING FOR A WHILE SO LET'S JUST SWITCH TO THE STORY OF...
SINBART THE SAILOR
AW, COME ON, GRAMPA! CAN'T I HAVE A LITTLE MORE ALLOWANCE? I BLEW IT ALL ON GETTING MY EAR PIERCED.
YOU SHOULD DO WHAT *I* DID WHEN *I* WAS YOUR AGE!

RIDE A DINOSAUR? INVENT FIRE? BORROW MONEY FROM ADAM AND EVE?

NO! I BECAME A ***SAILOR!*** STILL HAVE MY BOAT! IT'S YOURS IF YOU WANT IT!
THE SEA'S WHERE YOU'LL FIND YOUR FORTUNE!

SOON...
YOU GUYS SEE ANY CASH FLOATING IN THE OCEAN?
NOPE!
NOT YET, OH CAPTAIN, MY CAPTAIN!

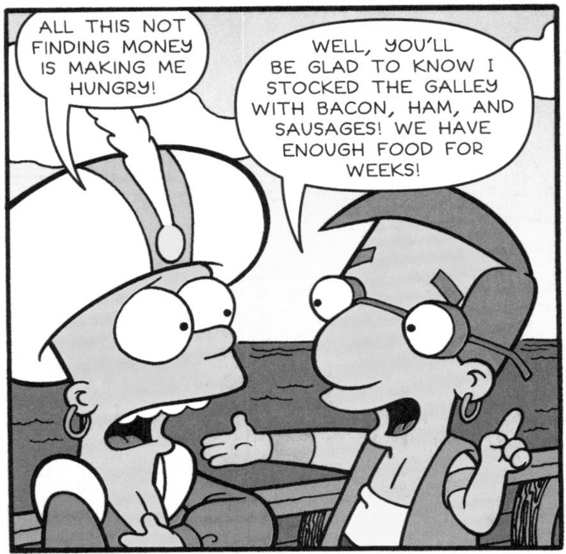
ALL THIS NOT FINDING MONEY IS MAKING ME HUNGRY!
WELL, YOU'LL BE GLAD TO KNOW I STOCKED THE GALLEY WITH BACON, HAM, AND SAUSAGES! WE HAVE ENOUGH FOOD FOR WEEKS!

MAYBE I SHOULDN'T HAVE TOLD THE DOG TO GUARD IT!
HAM
SAUSAGE
BACON
WHIMPER!
BACON
SAUSAGE

NONE OF THESE TREES POSSESS FRUIT. HOW ODD.
DOES ANYONE ELSE SMELL FISH?
I **SMELL** IT, BUT NONE ARE BITING!

OH, **ALLAH,** I KNOW I DON'T PRAY TO YOU MUCH, EXCEPT AT THE HOLIDAYS, BUT **PLEASE** LET US GET JUST ONE BITE.

I HAVE A BITE!
YOW! THAT ALLAH DOESN'T FOOL AROUND!

GLUB GLUB!*
*"GIVE ME THAT!"

GLUB GLUB!*
*"UP, BOY! UP!"

¡GASP!¡
SPLASH!

I'M PLEASED WE'RE BREATHING OXYGEN AGAIN, BUT WHAT DO WE DO NOW?
I'M GONNA TRY AND STEER HIM TOWARDS THAT BIG ISLAND OVER THERE!

MY RICE PADDY!

EEW! SEAWEED!

EXCUSE ME! I AM THE CHIEF CHEF TO THE EMPEROR OF JAPAN. HE'S GROWN BORED WITH OUR FOOD AND IS LOOKING FOR A NEW TASTE SENSATION. WHAT DO YOU CALL THIS CULINARY CREATION OF YOURS?
HMMM... RAW FISH WITH SEAWEED ON RICE?

I CALL IT A TACO!
WE'LL RUN IT BY MARKETING!
HEY, CHECK IT OUT!
MAN, I'M HUNGRY. I HOPE WE SLIDE PAST A DRIVE-THRU WINDOW.

ONE VOYAGE LATER...
SO, SINBART, DOES THIS ISLAND HAVE RICHES?
WELL, THERE'S GOOD NEWS, BAD NEWS, GOOD NEWS, BAD NEWS, AND GOOD NEWS.

WHAT'S THE GOOD NEWS?

THE ISLAND IS COVERED IN GIANT DIAMONDS.
WHAT'S THE BAD NEWS?

IT'S GUARDED BY GIANT SNAKES!
AND THE GOOD NEWS?
SSSS!

CAW!
THERE ARE GIANT SNAKE-EATING BIRDS!
AND THE BAD NEWS?

THE BIRDS EAT PEOPLE, TOO!
AND THE GOOD NEWS?

THEY FILLED UP ON MARTIN!
LET'S GO!

YET ANOTHER VOYAGE LATER...
CLINK!
CLINK!

H-HEY, SINBART, WHY ARE WE FIGHTING THESE SKELETONS AGAIN?
BECAUSE IT SURE LOOKS COOL!

OOPS! SORRY, LADY!
OH DEAR!
MAUDE!

AND ANOTHER VOY-- OH, YOU GET THE IDEA...
THERE'S NO TIME FOR LOVE, SINBART! WE HAVE TREASURE HUNTING TO DO!
I WANT YOU TO MEET MY FATHER, THE KING OF THE ISLAND!

HELLO, YOUNG MAN. WOULD YOU LIKE SOME SUNFLOWER SEEDS?
SURE!

OH, DAD!
WHAT? MUNCH!
NOW THAT YOU ACCEPTED MY FATHER'S GIFT OF SEEDS, WE'RE MARRIED! IT'S THE LAW OF THE ISLAND!

AW, MAN!
IS IT JUST ME OR DOES THAT ROCK LOOK LIKE IT'S GETTING BIGGER?

CRUNCH!
DAD!

YOU KNOW WHAT THIS MEANS, SINBART?
YOU'RE THE KING NOW!
I DIDN'T DO IT!

REALLY? COOL! IS THIS IS RICH KINGDOM?
NO, WE HAVE NO MONEY OR GOLD. ALL WE HAVE IS SEEDS!

SEEDS?! WHY?
BECAUSE WE ALSO TURN INTO BIRDS! IT'LL BE SO NICE HAVING A MAN AROUND THE NEST. HOW MANY EGGS DO YOU WANT TO HAVE WHEN WE GET OLDER? I'M THINKIING A DOZEN!

LET'S GO, MILHOUSE!
WAIT! WHY ARE YOU LEAVING? DON'T YOU LOVE ME?

SORRY, BABE. I'M A FREE SPIRIT! I CAN'T BE TIED DOWN.
SO WHAT YOU'RE REALLY SAYING IS...?

I WANT TO SEE OTHER CHICKS!
GROAN!

AND SO, SINBART SAILED OFF AND...
YOUR HIGHNESS?

AW! HE'S FAST ASLEEP!
ASLEEP NOTHING. HE'S DEAD! YOUR STORIES MUST HAVE BORED HIM TO DEATH!

HOORAY!
SMACK!
WE'RE FINALLY FREE!

DON'T BE SAD. YOU DON'T HAVE TO FEEL GUILTY!
OH, I DON'T. I CAME HERE TO ASSASSINATE HIM FOR EXECUTING MY SISTERS AFTER THEIR DATES WITH HIM.

WELL, GREAT PLAN KILLING HIM WITH YOUR DULL STORY!
MY PLAN WAS TO WAIT UNTIL HE WAS ASLEEP, TRANSFORM INTO AN ELEPHANT, AND STOMP HIM TO DEATH.

YEAH WELL, IT'S ALL GOOD.

YOU WERE RIGHT! THIS IS FUN TO WATCH. BUT DON'T THE MONKEYS MIND BEING IN A BOX LIKE THAT?
IT'S EVEN MORE FUN WHEN THEY GET **MAD!** I CALL IT A REALITY PROGRAM!
I'M HOME!
HI, MOM! HOW DID THE **AVENGING** GO?

I DON'T WANT TO TALK ABOUT IT. HOMER, IS THE GARBAGE STILL IN THE KITCHEN?
OH YEAH, I FORGOT TO TAKE IT OUT!
Duff
DRY

WHY AM I THE ONLY ONE IN THIS FAMILY WHO NEVER FORGETS ANYTHING?
THE END

Shakespeare

KING PRIAM, THE WAR AGAINST TROY HAS LASTED SEVEN LONG YEARS. WHAT SHALL WE DO?
OH WELL, IF AT FIRST YOU DON'T INVADE, TRY TROY AGAIN!
BARD BOILED
IAN BOOTHBY Story
JOHN COSTANZA Pencils
PHYLLIS NOVIN/HOWARD SHUM Inks
ART VILLANUEVA/JOEY MASON Colors
KAREN BATES Letters
MATT GROENING Shrew Tamer

BART, DO THE RIGHT LINES. YOU'RE RUINING "TROILUS AND CRESSIDA"!
C'MON, LIS, I'M JUST DOING A LITTLE IMPROV TO LIGHTEN THINGS UP.

OKAY, NOW WE NEED A LOCATION.
MY HOUSE!
THE KREMLIN!
AT A LESS BORING PLAY!

I HEARD VIDEO ARCADE! NOW WHAT'S THE REASON OUR DIRECTOR, LISA, SMELLS LIKE ROTTEN EGGS?
HEY!

I THINK SHAKESPEARE IS JUST FINE ON ITS OWN. DO IT RIGHT, OR WE'LL START THE WHOLE PLAY OVER AGAIN.
GROAN!

YOU KNOW, HOMER, I'M SO PROUD OF YOU. THIS IS THE FIRST SCHOOL PLAY YOU'VE BEEN ABLE TO STAY AWAKE FOR.

AND NOW, WITHOUT ANY MORE COLIN MOCHARIE-STYLE AD LIBS, HERE'S MORE SHAKESPEARE...
ZZZZZ
HOW TO SLEEP WITH YOUR EYES OPEN
HOW TO SLEEP WITH YOUR EYES OPEN

"ANTONY and CLEOPATRA"

I CAN'T BELIEVE HE'S ***LATE***. THIS COUNSELING WAS ***HIS*** IDEA!

FRIENDS, ROMANS, COUNTRYMEN, LEND ME YOUR EARS! I APOLOGIZE FOR MY ***TARDINESS!***
YOU SEE, THIS IS WHAT I MEAN! HE HAS ***NO RESPECT*** FOR MY ***NEEDS***.

I COULDN'T JUST LET ROME ***FALL,*** COULD I?
THE PLACE WAS A MESS. THE STREETS WERE COVERED IN ***LITTER,*** LEAVES IN THE ***AQUADUCTS,*** AND DON'T GET ME STARTED ON THE ***VOMITORIUMS!***

ALWAYS WITH THE OMITORIUMS! I KNEW HIS WAS A WASTE OF IME. YOU'RE THE ONE WITH "***ISSUES,***" NOT ME!
YOU SEE? THIS IS WHY THEY CALL HER "QUEEN OF DENIAL!"

IT'S "QUEEN OF ***THE NILE,***" AND DON'T TELL ME I HAVEN'T TRIED MY BEST IN THIS RELATIONSHIP. HE DOES NOTHING BUT ***COMPLAIN***.

MY ***SACRED CATS*** MAKE HIM ***SNEEZE,*** MY ***PYRAMIDS*** ARE ***TOO POINTY,*** AND NOW HE'S EVEN COMPLAINING ABOUT MY ***MILK BATHS!***

I'M ***LACTOSE INTOLERANT!*** I KISSED HER NECK AND WAS ***BLOATED*** FOR A WEEK!

SOMETIMES I THINK SHE TOOK CAESAR UP ON HIS REQUEST FOR HER TO ***KILL*** ME!

OH, SWEET RA, WILL YOU EVER LET THAT GO? I'LL TELL YOU HIS PROBLEM. A **FEAR OF COMMITMENT**.
NOT WANTING TO BE **BURIED ALIVE** WITH YOU WHEN YOU DIE ISN'T A FEAR OF COMMITMENT!

AND TO TOP IT ALL OFF, HE **FORGOT** OUR **ANNIVERSARY**.

DID I?
OH, ANTONY! YOU REMEMBERED!

AN **ASP!** OH, YOU SHOULDN'T HAVE.
THESE ARE SO EXPENSIVE TO GET **POISON-FREE**.
EXCUSE ME?

GAAAAH!
LUNGE!

SO, UM...ASIDE FROM THE **FATAL VENOM**, HOW DO YOU LIKE THE GIFT?
IT'S LIKE EVERYTHING ELSE IN THIS RELATIONSHIP, ANTONY...
...IT **BITES!**

"JULIUS CAESAR"

HAPPY FEAST OF LUPERCAL, MR. CAESAR.
AH, THE PEOPLE LOVE ME. DO THEY NOT, BRUTUS?
WE ALL DO, SIR.

!
SWISH!
THUNK!
OH, A COIN WITH MY FACE ON IT! THAT'S GOOD LUCK!

"RENDER UNTO CAESAR WHAT IS CAESAR'S," I ALWAYS SAY. YOU KNOW, WE SHOULD BUILD A FACTORY THAT JUST RENDERS THINGS TO ME. WE COULD CALL IT A RENDERING PLANT.
EXCELLENT IDEA, SIR. BUT FOR NOW, THE SENATE IS WAITING FOR US.

AHOY-HOY, SENATE!
HAIL, CAESAR!

OH, MARK ANTONY, HOW ARE THINGS WITH THAT SAUCY EGYPTIAN YOU'VE BEEN COURTING?
DON'T ASK.

BEFORE WE GET TO BUSINESS, I WANT TO HOLD A **PICNIC** IN HONOR OF MYSELF TOMORROW. WHAT WILL THE **WEATHER** BE LIKE?
HAIL, CAESAR.
YES, HAIL YOURSELF. BUT WHAT'S THE **WEATHER** GOING TO BE LIKE?

HAIL, CAESAR.
OKAY, HELLO TO YOU TOO! ALL I WANT TO KNOW IS... **THE WEATHER!**
HAIL... CAESAR!

OKAY, FORGET THE WEATHER! LET'S TALK ABOUT **THE MEAL**.
I WANT THAT **DELICIOUS SALAD** YOU MADE THE LAST TIME WITH THE **ROMAINE LETTUCE**. WHAT WAS IT CALLED AGAIN?
CAESAR.

YES, WHAT WAS IT **CALLED**?
CAESAR.

HAVE HIM **FLOGGED!**
SIR, THAT'S **VERY PAINFUL**. HAVE MERCY.
OH, DEAR!
VERY WELL, KILL HIM **FIRST**.

MAN, THAT GUY'S NUTS!
YOU SAID IT, CALIGULA!

I WAS TALKING TO THE OTHER SENATOR.
?

NOW, IF THERE IS NO FURTHER BUSINESS...

SWISH!
...AH, ANOTHER COIN!
ROAR!

MAN, I WASTED MY LAST LION!
DOES THAT MEAN WE CHRISTIANS CAN GO? OR DO YOU HAVE ANY OTHER ANIMALS YOU'D LIKE TO FEED US TO?

WELL, I'M OFF TO THE BATHS. WILL I SEE YOU THERE, BRUTUS?
YOU KNOW YOU WILL, SIR!

I'M HAVING SECOND THOUGHTS ABOUT THE ASSASSINATION.
BRUTUS.
NO WAY, BLUTO.

WHATEVER, THERE'S NO BACKING OUT NOW! TONIGHT, WE KILL JULIUS CAESAR AND MARK ANTONY!
HEY!

OOPS! NO, NOT YOU! I MEAN MARK... UM...MARK...
...MARK HAMILL!

A SHORT WHILE LATER...
OKAY, BACK TO ROME!
GUYS & DOLLS
THE BLACK PEARL

MAYBE WE CAN JUST LET HIM OFF WITH A STERN WARNING IN THE SUGGESTION BOX.

THE SENATE! WHAT, IS THIS SOME SORT OF PARTY IN MY HONOR?
UM...KIND OF ...A SURPRISE PARTY.

:SIGH.: LET'S DO THIS QUICKLY.

SURPRISE!
STAB!

OOPS.

WHAT'S WITH ALL THIS LYING AROUND HOLDING YOUR STOMACHS? WHERE ARE THE BALLOONS? WHERE'S THE CAKE?
HE WAS TOO THIN. WE ALL MISSED HIM AND STABBED EACH OTHER. THANK, JUPITER!

HERE YOU GO.
WHAT? WHERE DID YOU GET A CAKE?

I ALWAYS CARRY ONE WITH ME...JUST IN CASE.
I ATE ONE PIECE, BUT PLANNING ASSASSINATIONS MAKES ME HUNGRY, SO I...
HOLD THE CHARIOT! TWO PIECES ARE MISSING.
DON'T SAY IT.

...ATE TWO, BRUTUS.
:GROAN!:

THANK YOU ALL FOR SHOWING UP TO AGINCOURT SO EARLY.
TODAY WE GO INTO BATTLE ⁙GA-HOY⁙!
"HENRY V"

YOU ARE MY **BAND OF BROTHERS**. FOR ANYONE WHO **FIGHTS** HERE TODAY SHALL BE MY BROTHER.
THIS IS THANKS TO SOME **SIMPLE ADJUSTMENTS** I MADE TO YOUR **DNA** WHILE YOU WERE **SLEEPING!**

WE FEW, WE ARE THE **HAPPY FEW**. AND AS MOST OF YOU ARE **SLAUGHTERED,** THERE WILL BE FEWER PEOPLE, AND SO BY THE **LAWS OF THERMODYNAMICS AND PROBABILITY**, THE **REMAINING HAPPINESS** WILL BE **DISTRIBUTED** TO THE LIVING, MAKING THEM VERY HAPPY INDEED.
HAPPIER THAN **THE DEAD,** ANYWAY ⁙GA-HEY⁙!

YOU WILL **PROUDLY** TALK OF THIS DAY TO YOUR CHILDREN AND YOUR CHILDREN'S CHILDREN.
UNLESS YOU GET YOUR **TONGUE CUT OUT** AS A **TROPHY** FOR OUR ENEMIES, AS IS THEIR CUSTOM.

AND THOSE WHO ARE ASLEEP RIGHT NOW WILL RUE THAT THEY WEREN'T HERE, BUT STUCK AT HOME IN THEIR **COMFY BEDS**.
WITH THEIR FLUFFY PILLOWS, SNOOZE ALARMS, AND SWEET TEDDY STRAIGHT FROM THE DRYER. WATCH OUT FOR THE **HOT BUTTON EYES,** SWEET GLAVIN!

AND NOW TO THE **BLOODBATH** WITH THE **GORE** AND THE **MUD** AND THE "**OH MY GOSH, IT HURTS ME!**"

THIS FIELD IS **EMPTIER** THAN MY **SOCIAL CALENDAR**. THE **COWARDS** HAVE ALL GONE HOME.
WELL, IT'S BACK TO BED FOR ME, TOO. THOSE **PEP TALKS** ALWAYS **DO THE TRICK!**

JUST STOP ***SWEARING*** ALREADY! YOU'LL WAKE UP ***MY PARENTS***!

"Romeo and Juliet"

I STUBBED MY TOE ON YOUR @#!! GARDEN GNOME!

LISTEN AND HEAR THE ***SAD STORY*** OF ***TWO STAR-CROSSED LOVERS***.

WHATEVER THAT MEANS.

HOP!

HOP!

HOP!

VERONA IS A NICE PLACE FOR PEOPLE TO LIVE AND STUFF...
HELLO, YOUNG MAN!
GOODDAY TO YOU, FAIR NARRATOR!
...EXCEPT FOR THE *FAMILY FEUD*.

"IN THIS CORNER WE HAVE THE CAPULET FAMILY, READY FOR ACTION."
I'LL TEACH YOU TO *BITE YOUR THUMB* AT ME!
LET
SIGH
I WAS JUST BITING MY THUMB.

"AND THE MONTAGUES. UM... WHERE ARE YOUR FAMILY?"
IN *JAIL*. THE *BAIL BONDSMAN* WOULDN'T RETURN THEIR CALL AFTER DAD BOUNCED THAT LAST CHECK TO HIM.
JUST GET ON WITH THE STORY, OR I'LL POUND YA!
GUE

SO THEIR *FORBIDDEN LOVE* WAS A *SECRET*. LIKE THE LOVE BETWEEN MY OCTOPUS, MR. INKS, AND MY GIRAFFE, SPOT.

OH, ROMEO, DOST THOU *LOVE* ME?
Y'KNOW, WHATEVER.
CAN I COME UP THERE AND *KISS* YA?

IT IS ALL I WISH FAIR ROMEO, BUT MY **NURSE** MIGHT HEAR AND TELL MY PARENTS!
YEAH, LIKE I CARE. I HAVE TO CHANGE YOUR FATHER'S **BED-PAN**.

HE'S SICK?
NO, JUST REALLY **LAZY**.

I HAVE TO GET READY FOR MY **WEDDING** TONIGHT. I'M GOING TO TRY AND GET OUT OF THAT, AND I'LL KISS YOU AFTER. SEE YOU LATER?
YEAH, OKAY I GUESS.

DUDE, WHAT'S HAPPENED TO YOU?
YOU WERE LISTENING?
YEAH, AND YOU'RE MORE **WHIPPED** THAN MERINGUE PIE.

AT LEAST MY GIRLFRIEND IS **REAL**.
KELLY'S REAL. SHE JUST LIVES IN... UM...CANADA.
LAST TIME YOU SAID IT WAS **ICELAND**.
THAT'S **IT! LET'S DUEL!**

CHILL, TYBALT. YOUR PAROLE OFFICER SAID NO MORE DEATH DUELS AND...**OW!**
HEY, MERCUTIO, GET OUT OF MY **SWORD'S WAY!**
STAB!

YOU KILLED HIM, YOU JERK. TAKE THAT!
OW!
STAB!

SORRY I'M LATE. DID I MISS ANYTHING?

MEANWHILE...
DAUGHTER, OPEN THIS DOOR, YOUR FIANCÉ IS HERE. TIME FOR YOUR WEDDING.
KNOCK! KNOCK!
CAN WE HURRY THIS UP? I HAVE A GAME OF HIDE AND SEEK I SHOULD REALLY GET BACK TO.

OH RIGHT, THE WEDDING. WOULDN'T MISS IT FOR THE WORLD.
FAKING YOUR DEATH THE E-Z WAY

WE'RE COMING IN!
ISN'T IT BAD LUCK FOR ME TO SEE HER BEFORE THE CEREMONY?

GASP!
I GUESS SO.

AND SO...
HEY, ROMEO!
SORRY TO HEAR ABOUT, JULIET.
HUH? WHAT ARE YOU TALKING ABOUT?

SHORTLY...
OW! I SHOWED YOU WHERE HER TOMB IS. WHAT ARE YOU HITTING ME FOR?
I'M WORKING THROUGH SOME GRIEF.
WHUMPH!

AW, MAN, IT'S TRUE! SHE'S DEAD.
OH, MY LOVE. ALL THE THINGS I NEVER GOT A CHANCE TO SAY. WELL, NOW I WILL!

I THINK WE SHOULD SEE OTHER PEOPLE.
IT'S NOT YOU, IT'S ME. WELL YOU BEING DEAD AND EVERYTHING... I GUESS IT IS YOU. I HOPE WE CAN STILL BE FRIENDS.
IT'D BE COOL HAVING A CORPSE FOR A PAL.

YOU JERK! I'M DEAD, AND YOU BREAK UP WITH ME!
AHHHH! A ZOMBIE!
I WAS JUST FAKING BEING DEAD TO BE WITH YOU.

I DIDN'T KNOW THAT! WHAT DID YOU EXPECT ME TO DO?
DRINK POISON, THEN I'D THINK YOU WERE DEAD, AND STAB MYSELF IN THE HEART!
IT'D BE THE MOST ROMANTIC STORY EVER.

I COULD STAB YOU WITH MY SWORD IF YOU'D LIKE.
ARRRGH! YOU ARE SO FRUSTRATING!

YOU KNOW, I DON'T THINK I'LL EVER UNDERSTAND GIRLS.
I HEAR YA. WANNA PLAY HIDE AND SEEK?
YOU'RE ON!

"The Two Gentlemen Of Verona"

RICHARD III

NOW IS THE WINTER OF OUR *DISCONTENT*.

I MEAN HAVE YOU SEEN *OUR NUMBERS*? WE'RE BEING *SLAUGHTERED* BY ALL THE *CHRISTMAS SPECIALS!*

HERE'S TEN GRAND. BREAK RUDOLPH'S KNEECAPS!
BUT YOUR MAJESTY, HE IS A *PUPPET*.
THEN CLIP HIS STRINGS. GEEZ, DO THEY EVEN TRAIN YOU GOONS ANYMORE? NOW SCRAM, I'M ON IN ONE MINUTE.

:SIGH.: WAS IT ALL WORTHWHILE? SURE, I'M *THE KING OF COMEDY*, BUT ALL THOSE I'VE CRUSHED ON MY WAY TO THE TOP...
...WAS IT ALL WORTH IT FOR THE *MONEY*, *FAME*, AND *POWER*?

HEH, HEH! MAN I ALWAYS MAKE MYSELF LAUGH WITH THAT JOKE!

HEY, HEY! IT'S GREAT TO BE DOING THE SHOW HERE IN *BOSWORTH! WHO DO YOU LOVE*?!
KING RICHARD!
LET'S START WITH AN "*ITCHY AND SCRATCHY CARTOON*"!

ITCHY & SCRATCHY IN: "TITUS ANDRONICUS"

AAAH!
RETURN TO SENDER

GRRRRR!
WELCOME TO ROME
POKE!

HAPPY TRUCE DAY
MMMMMM!

YAAAA!

YOU KNOW ITCHY, I LIKE VIOLENCE AS MUCH AS THE NEXT GUY, BUT WHOEVER WROTE THIS IS REALLY MESSED UP.
WORD!

AW, MAN, I'M LOSING THEM.
TIME TO DO **THE COWBOY SKETCH**.
BOOOOO!

HOWDY, Y'ALL! THE BANK'S BEEN ROBBED, AND I THINK THAT DURN HOMBRE **OTHELLO** DID IT. WHY DO I THINK THAT?
I'VE GOT A **HUNCH**!

OOOOKAY, RIGHT TO **THE STUNT RIDING**.
KRUSTY I WOULDN'T DO THAT.
SPROING!

GAH!
WHOA!
WHY DID HE KILL THAT HORSE, MOMMY?
AAAAH!
WHAM!

A HORSE! A HORSE! MY KINGDOM FOR TWO **NON-UNION ACTORS** TO PLAY A HORSE.
RICHARD, I'M HERE TO KILL YOU.

AND BY YOU, I MEAN YOUR SHOW. I'M THE **NEW HEAD OF PROGRAMMING** AND YOUR SHOW IS BEING PUT ON **HIATUS** INDEFINITELY FOR **RETOOLING**.
SIDESHOW RICHMOND? BUT I CRUSHED YOU ON MY WAY TO THE TOP.
THEN CONSIDER THIS YOUR **DAILY IRONY SUPPLIMENT**.

YOU'LL NEVER FIND A **REPLACEMENT** FOR ME.
WE ALREADY HAVE. IT'S A NEW SHOW CALLED "KING LEAR."
WHEN'S THAT START?
RIGHT NOW.

MAN, BEING A KING IS SO BORING.
"KING LEAR"

GONERIL, REGAN, CORDELIA! WE'RE GOING TO PLAY A GAME!

A GAME? WHAT AN EXCELLENT IDEA, FATHER! TAG? CHESS? HUNTING PEASANTS FOR SPORT?
BETTER!
THIS IS A GAME CALLED, "WHO LOVES DADDY BEST?"

HOW MUCH DO YOU LOVE ME, GONERIL?

AWWWW, THAT'S SWEET! BUT HERE'S A TIP, MAYBE YOU CAN DO SOME STRETCHING EXCERCISES TO GET THOSE LITTLE ARMS A BIT FARTHER APART.

HOW ABOUT YOU, REGAN?
SO GLAD YOU ASKED, FATHER!
CLAP! CLAP!
HOW MUCH DO I LOVE THEE? MORE THAN ALL THE STARS IN HEAVEN. MORE THAN ALL THE GRAINS OF SAND ON THE BEACH. MORE THAN ALL THE BEADS OF SWEAT ON A SUBSTITUTE TEACHER'S FOREHEAD. WORDS CANNOT EXPRESS MY LOVE, AND SO I SHALL END THIS SENTENCE...NOW.

THE MONKEYS WERE A NICE TOUCH.
YOUR PRAISE HUMBLES ME!

HOW ABOUT YOU, CORDELIA?
I LOVE YOU, FATHER.

BUT HOW MUCH?
I LOVE YOU AS A DAUGHTER LOVES A FATHER. I LOVE YOU AS MUCH AS YOU LOVE ME.

THAT'S ALL? I'VE NEVER BEEN SO INSULTED!
GO TO THE ROOM!

MY ROOM?
NO! THE BANISHMENT ROOM!

BANISHMENT ROOM
I DIDN'T EVEN KNOW WE HAD A BANISHMENT ROOM.

BANISHMENT ROOM
AAAAAAAH!

GOOD DECISION, FATHER!

THIS JUST IN, KING LEAR HAS BANISHED HIS DAUGHTER CORDELIA.
IN THIS REPORTER'S OPINION...A BAD MOVE, AS SHE WAS HIS ONLY TRULY LOVING CHILD. THIS IS LORD KENT REPORTING.

YOU ARE SO BANISHED!
YOU CAN'T BANISH ME! I'M GOING TO EMIGRATE!
I HAVE NO IDEA WHAT THAT MEANS.

TOSS!
AAAAAAH!

DON'T WORRY, FATHER. WE'LL TAKE CARE OF YOU THE WAY YOU *DESERVE* TO BE TREATED.
THANK YOU, MY CHILDREN.

ONE WEEK LATER...
I FEEL *AWFUL,* LIKE I'VE AGED *FORTY YEARS*. WHAT HAVE YOU BEEN *FEEDING* ME?
WAAAAH!

IT'S NOT *POISON,* SO THAT YOU'LL BE GONE SOON, AND I'LL TAKE OVER, IF THAT'S WHAT YOU'RE THINKING. NOW SHUT UP AND CHANGE GON'S DIAPERS!

WHAT HAVE I DONE?

YOU WERE RIGHT, KENT. I AM SO SORRY FOR NOT LISTENING TO YOU TOO, GENTLE FOOL.
WHAT ARE YOU TALKING ABOUT? WHEN WAS I IN THIS STORY?
WE HAD TO *CUT YOUR SCENE*. IT WASN'T *PLAYING WELL* WITH THE 19-35 *DEMOGRAPHIC*.

I MUST *FIND* MY DAUGHTER. MY SWEET LOVING CHILD!
SOME DOGS WERE CHEWING ON SOMETHING IN THE BUSHES.

OH BY THE GODS, NO!

BLOW, WINDS, AND CRACK YOUR CHEEKS. RAGE, BLOW--

HOLD IT!
WHAT?

SHE'S TOTALLY FAKING TO GET ATTENTION! SHE DID THE SAME THING TO ME!

AAAAH!
ROMEO! YOU SHOULDN'T EVEN BE HERE!
TOLD YA!

YOU ARE SO RUDE...SO RUDE...SO RUDE...

ZZZZZZZZZ
THAT IS SO RUDE! I DON'T BELIEVE IT! THE ENTIRE AUDIENCE IS ASLEEP!

OUR PLAY IS A FAILURE.
MY EYES ARE LEAKING!

WHY ARE YOU SO HAPPY, BART?

WHILE YOU WERE WHINING, I GOT ALL OUR PARENTS' WALLETS.
BUT THAT'S STEALING!
AS LONG AS THEY'RE SLEEPING, IT'S JUST A MIDSUMMER NIGHT'S DREAM.

YOU LITTLE PUCK.
LISA, PLEASE! THERE ARE CHILDREN HERE!

NOW, WHO'S UP FOR SOME ICE CREAM?
YAY!

D THUS...
AS YOU LICK IT!
ICE CREAM PARL
I'M STILL SAD THAT THE PLAY WAS A *FLOP,* BUT THIS ICE CREAM IS DELICIOUS.
WELL, YOU KNOW WHAT I ALWAYS SAY, LIS...
...*ALL'S WELL THAT ENDS WELL!*
Ye End

BIBLE STORIES

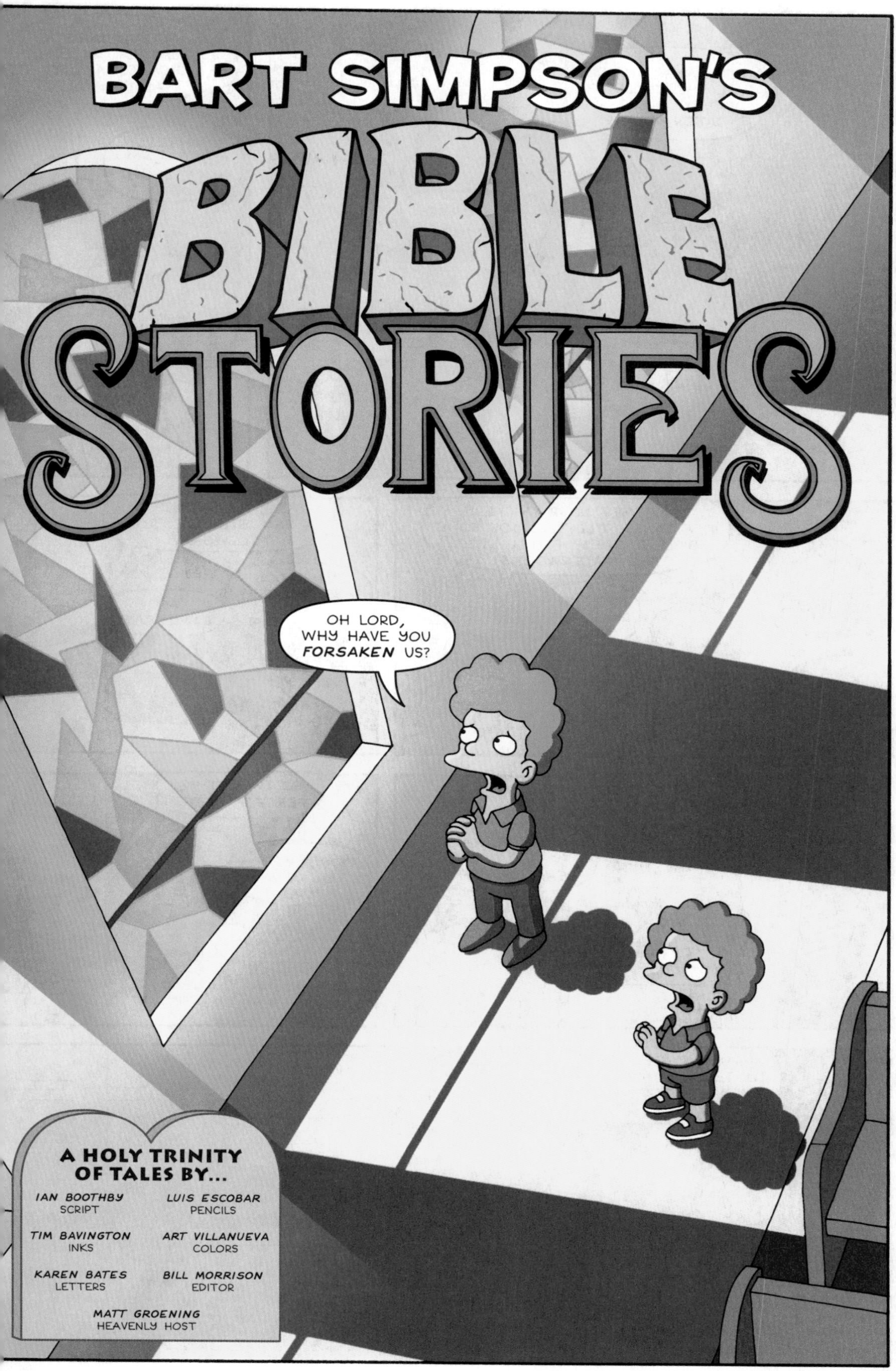

BART SIMPSON'S BIBLE STORIES

OH LORD, WHY HAVE YOU *FORSAKEN* US?

A HOLY TRINITY OF TALES BY...

IAN BOOTHBY SCRIPT
LUIS ESCOBAR PENCILS
TIM BAVINGTON INKS
ART VILLANUEVA COLORS
KAREN BATES LETTERS
BILL MORRISON EDITOR
MATT GROENING HEAVENLY HOST

HEY, WHAT'S WITH ALL THE *YELLING*? DID TODD SEE A *CATERPILLAR*?
WORSE!

SUNDAY SCHOOL TEACHER CALLED IN *SICK* TODAY, SO IT WAS CANCELLED.
WHAT'LL WE DO BART? *WHAT'LL WE DO?!!*

DON'T GET YOUR KNICKERS IN A TWIST. *I'LL* TELL YOU SOME BIBLE STORIES, IF IT'LL STOP *THE WATERWORKS!*
YOU'VE READ THE BIBLE?

WELL, I'VE PICKED UP A *FEW STORIES* FROM *TELEVISION*.
BUT DADDY SAYS *CABLE TV* IS *EVIL*.
AND *EXPENSIVE*.

LOOK, GOD MADE *EVERYTHING*, RIGHT?
YES.
YES.
AND SO HE MADE TV. AND GOD IS *PERFECT*, RIGHT?

SO *TV* MUST BE *PERFECT*. RIGHT?
I GUESS SO.
OKAY, BART! TELL US A STORY.

PULL UP A PEW, AND I'LL TELL YOU A TALE OF A FAMILY NOT *TOO DIFFERENT* FROM YOURS OR MINE.
WELL, NOT TOO DIFFERENT FROM *MINE*.

"THE PRODIGAL SON"

HOW'S YOUR SQUISHEE?
AND WE'RE JUST GETTING STARTED!
GREAT! YOU CAN REALLY TASTE THE MYRRH!
NEW SQUISHEE FLAVORS - FRANKINCENSE AND MYRRH
MILK AND HONEY- HALF PRICE BLOWOUT

YOU'RE GONNA LOVE THIS NEXT PLACE. THE PARTY NEVER ENDS!

TEMPORARILY CLOSED DUE TO ACT OF GOD
AWW...

DON'T WORRY, THERE'S ANOTHER PLACE JUST AS GOOD DOWN THE STREET.

TEMPORARILY CLOSED DUE TO ACT OF GOD
OH, FOR CRYING OUT LOUD!

NOW YOU SAY YOUR WIFE WAS ASSAULTED?
NO! I KEEP TELLING YOU, SHE WAS SALTED!
JUST LOOK AT HER!

SALT, EH? THAT'S GONNA BE MURDER ON MY HIGH BLOOD PRESSURE.
ANY IDEA WHO DID IT?
SURE! SAME GUY WHO BLEW UP THE TOWN!
KRA-BOOM!
LISTEN, I'D LOVE TO HELP YOU BUT LOOK AT THE TIME ON THAT SUNDIAL.
SEE YA!
WHAT SUNDIAL?
WHAT DO YOU WANNA DO NOW?
WHY DO I ALWAYS HAVE TO THINK OF EVERY-THING?
OKAY, LET'S PLAY STICKBALL!
COMING SOON
TOWER OF BABEL
HEAVENLY VIEWS
SUITES NOW AVAILABLE

FINE! GRAB A STICK!
YANK!

TOO THIN!

HOW ABOUT THIS ONE?
TOO THICK!

PERFECT!
PLAY BALL!

RUUUUUUMBLE!
UH, OH!

SHHH-WUMFFF!
CRASH!
BAM!

MAMA MIA!
PARDON? TU PARLE FRANCAIS?
法語是什麼？
THEY MUST HAVE ALL **HIT THEIR HEADS!**
I DIDN'T DO IT, NOBODY SAW ME DO IT. YOU CAN'T PROVE ANYTHING!

WOW! A ***FORTUNE TELLER!*** LET'S GO IN!
FORTUNE TELLER 100% ACCURATE OR YOUR MONEY BACK

I PREDICT THAT YOU WILL SOON BE ***ROBBED,*** LITTLE DUDE.

YOINK!
LIKE TAKING ALMS FROM A SAMARITAN!

SO WE'RE BROKE. WHO NEEDS MONEY TO HAVE A GOOD TIME?

WANNA WATCH THAT GUY GET STONED?
NAH!
OW! MAN, THIS ISN'T AS MUCH FUN AS I THOUGHT IT'D BE! OW!
BONK!
THUMP!

HEY, WHY DON'T WE...
UH, EXCUSE ME.

HEY, IS THAT A BAG OF GOLD?
YES. YES IT IS.
NEED A BEST FRIEND?
YES. YES I DO.

FINE! WHO NEEDS YOU?
I'VE GOT NEW FRIENDS. THE...UH... LEPERS!

YOU WISH!
AS IF!

YOU COULD HELP WITH THE PLOW SOMETIME!
THAT WOULD BE THE SIN OF COVETING MY WIFE WHO HAS THE JOB OF MY OX AND MY ASS.

I'D LIKE TO READ THOSE COMMANDMENTS YOU'RE ALWAYS QUOTING SOMETIME.
WELL, WELL! LOOK WHO'S BACK!

DAD, I... I SPENT ALL MY MONEY FOOLISHLY AND SELFISHLY. I'M REALLY SORRY.

WIFE! KILL THE FATTED CALF FOR A FEAST IN OUR SON'S HONOR!
WHAT?!!! WHILE HE'S BEEN OUT HAVING A GOOD TIME, I'VE BEEN SLAVING ON THIS FARM!

DAUGHTER, WE LOVE YOU, BUT THERE'S MORE JOY IN HEAVEN FOR ONE LOST SHEEP THAT COMES BACK TO THE FOLD THAN FOR ALL THAT STAY.
BUT HE DOES THIS WITH HIS ALLOWANCE EVERY WEEK!

YOU REALLY JUST DO THIS AS AN EXCUSE FOR FATTED CALF, DON'T YOU?
CAN'T TALK... HONORING SON BY EATING!
GOD BLESS US, EVERYONE!
YEA, VERILY!

"ABRAHAM'S SACRIFICE"

YEARS PASSED AND GOD SPOKE TO ABRAHAM AGAIN...
ABE! You must offer your son as a BURNT SACRIFICE to prove your FAITH!

SACRIFICE MY SON! GOT IT!
WHO ARE YOU TALKING TO DADDY?
OH, NO ONE.

MORE TIME PASSED...
Um... Abraham, about that sacrifice.
RIGHT, RIGHT, I'M ON IT.

EVEN MORE TIME PASSED...
ABE! I won't say this again! sacrifice your son NOW!!
WELL, THIS IS THE FIRST I'VE HEARD OF IT.

SO WHERE ARE WE GOING?
MORAIH.
ISN'T MY BROTHER, ISHMAEL, COMING ALONG?
NO, I JUST NEED ONE OF YOU.

SO LONG! DON'T BE A STRANGER!
CALL ME, ISHMAEL!

I'M HUNGRY. WHEN WE GET WHERE WE'RE GOING, IS THERE GOING TO BE A BARBEQUE?
YOU MIGHT SAY THAT!

WELL, HERE WE ARE!
A MOUNTAIN? AWWW! YOU DIDN'T SAY THERE'D BE CLIMBING!

QUIT YOUR BELLYACHING AND HAVE A BEER. IT'LL REFRESH YOU, AND THE ALCOHOL WILL HELP YA BURN QUICKER.
HUH?
DID I SAY BURN QUICKER? I MEANT BURNS IS A QUAKER!

NOW THIS MAKES NO HISTORICAL SENSE AT ALL!
GOD WORKS IN MYSTERIOUS WAYS, SIR.

STOP THAT PANTING AND HELP ME BUILD A FIRE!
GASP! WHEEZE!

SOON...
WELL SON, I'VE GOT SOMETHING TO TELL YOU!
I DON'T GET IT, DAD. WHERE'S THE LAMB FOR THE BARBECUE?

AND SO, ABRAHAM EXPLAINED EVERYTHING...
WHAT?!!!

WAIT! WAIT! HEAR ME OUT! IT'S NOT LIKE I'M NOT GIVING YOU A CHOICE!

YOU CAN EITHER REJECT GOD AND WALK ALL THE WAY DOWN THE MOUNTAIN, OR I CAN CARRY YOU HOME IN THIS NICE COMFY URN!

IT IS A LONG WALK.
I WISH WE BELONGED TO ONE OF THOSE NON-SACRIFICING RELIGIONS.

THAT KIND OF TALK CAN LEAD TO A PERSON BURNING IN HELL!
AND THERE'S ONLY ONE WAY TO AVOID THAT HORRIBLE FATE!

GET INTO THAT FIRE!

SIGH
OKAY, I'LL DO IT!

Abraham! You and your son have passed my test of faith! He doesn't need to jump into the fire.
GOTCHA!

WHAT'S THAT, DAD?
GOD SAYS TO JUMP INTO THE FIRE.
YOU GOT IT!

NO! NO! I said DON'T jump into the fire!
WELL YOU REALLY NEED TO SPEAK UP AND CUT BACK ON THE REVERB!
SON, YOU...

UH, OH.

SON, WE'VE DONE GOD'S CONFUSING WORK, AND I'VE NEVER BEEN MORE PROUD OF YOU.
THANKS FOR PUTTING ME OUT, DAD.

LISTEN, SON, YOU'VE HELPED ME OUT, SO IF THERE'S ANYTHING I CAN DO FOR YOU, JUST NAME IT!
WELL...I'D REALLY LIKE THAT BIKE I NEVER GOT FOR CHRISTMAS.

CHRISTMAS?!! THIS IS THE OLD TESTAMENT! THAT IS SIMPLY TOO MUCH! THEY'RE NOT EVEN TRYING ANYMORE!
I QUIT!
YOU GOT IT, SON!
SO LET IT BE WRITTEN. SO LET IT BE DONE!

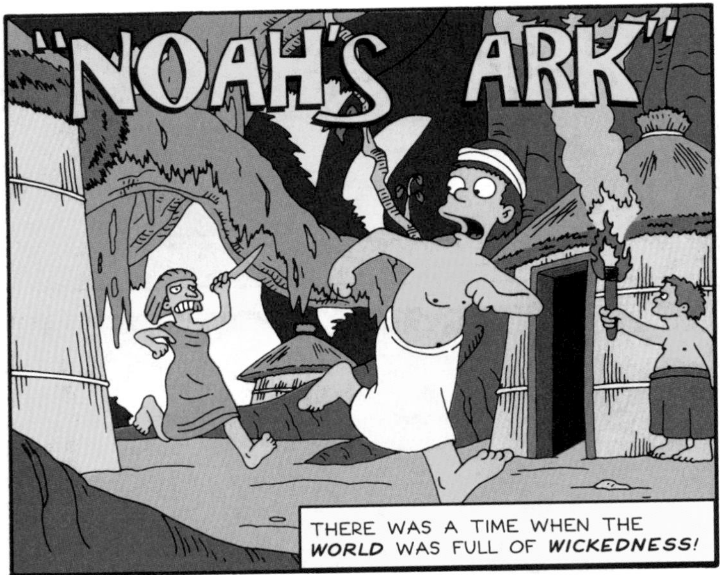
"NOAH'S ARK"
THERE WAS A TIME WHEN THE WORLD WAS FULL OF WICKEDNESS!

FALSE IDOLS WERE WORSHIPPED...

...AND NO ONE RECYCLED.

GOD SPOKE TO NOAH, THE ONLY GOOD MAN ON EARTH, AND TOLD HIM TO BUILD AN ARK, SO HIS FAMILY WOULD BE SPARED FROM THE GREAT FLOOD TO COME.
WELL, I WAS GONNA USE ALL THIS WOOD TO MAKE A PATIO AND GAZEBO, BUT, HEY, YOU'RE THE BOSS!

NOAH TOLD HIS WIFE AND SONS ABOUT THE RAIN TO COME, NOT KNOWING THAT HIS NEXT DOOR NEIGHBOR WAS EAVESDROPPING.
SO WE'VE GOT TO START BUILDING RIGHT AWAY SHEM, HAM.
OKILLY DOKILLY, DADDYLLY-DOO!
MMM... HAM!

WAIT! WHAT WAS THAT PART ABOUT EVERYONE DROWNING?

SAY, NOAH, OLD PAL, CAN MY FAMILY COME ON YOUR BOAT WITH YOU?
NO.
HOW ABOUT JUST ME AND THE WIFE?
NO.
HOW ABOUT...
WHAT PART OF NOAH DON'T YOU UNDERSTAND?!!
SORRY ABOUT BEING SUCH A SNAPPING TURTLE THERE, NEIGHBOR, BUT THIS DEADLINE HAS ME WOUND UP TIGHTER THAN AN ANGEL'S HARP STRING.
SO WE CAN COME WITH YOU?
SORRY. NO CAN-DIDDLY-DO.
HOW COME THEY GET EVERY ANIMAL ON EARTH, AND I CAN'T EVEN HAVE A PONY?

SO NED'S GOT A BIG BOAT, AND ANIMALS SEEM TO LIKE HIM. IT'S NOT THE END OF THE WORLD.
ACTUALLY, IT IS.

WE ALL KNOW THE STORY SO LET'S SKIP AHEAD A MINUTE OR TWO...
I TOLD YOU WE SHOULD HAVE BEEN NICER TO THEM!

RAIN, RAIN GO AWAY. HAVE THE APOCALYPSE SOME OTHER DAY.
WHO ARE YOU PRAYING TO?
GOD'S BOSS, I GUESS.

OKAY, DON'T PANIC EVERYONE! I'VE GOT A PLAN!
JUST WHEN I THOUGHT WE COULDN'T GET ANY MORE DOOMED!

HOMER? THE PLAN?
WHY YOU LITTLE...!
GAAK!

OH RIGHT!
COUGH!

HEY! GRIFFINS!
YO! JACKALOPES!
DID YOU HEAR SOMETHING?
IT CAME FROM BEHIND THAT BUSH.
LET US GO BACK THERE AND SEE WHAT IT IS, SHALL WE?

HURRY UP NOW, THE RAIN'S REALLY COMING DOW-DIDDLY-OWN!
MOOSE...FLYING SQUIRREL...
JACKALOPES... GRIFFINS...THAT'S ALL OF THE ANIMALS, DADDY.
ENJOY YOUR TRIP!
SHUT UP, NOAH.
HUH?
♫ GOD SAID TO NOAH THERE'S GONNA BE A FLOODY FLOODY! ♫
BOYS COME INSIDE AND LET THE PEOPLE DROWN IN PEACE!
GOODBYE, ROSE.
I'LL ALWAYS REMEMBER YOU, JACK.
WORST WRATH OF GOD EVER!

HOW ABOUT THIS! A FLOOR ALL TO OURSELVES!
UM...DAD, ACCORDING TO THIS BLUEPRINT WE'RE ON THE **MANURE FLOOR**.

CALL IT WHAT YOU WANT, BUT IT'S DRY, AND WE'RE UNDROWNED.
WHY ARE ALL THOSE ANIMALS **SQUATTING** ON THAT GRID ABOVE US?

AAAAAAH!

FINE! SO THAT DIDN'T WORK OUT. WE'LL BE SAFE HIDDEN HERE WITH THE ANIMALS. HEY, WHERE'S LISA?
SHE'S **DEBATING** WITH THE CARNIVORES AGAIN.

ALL I'M SAYING IS THAT YOU SHOULD AT LEAST **CONSIDER** A VEGETARIAN LIFESTYLE.
I HEAR YOU, BUT WHAT PART DOES **EVOLUTIONARY BIOLOGY** PLAY IN ALL THIS?

I CAN'T TAKE THE STINK ANY-MORE. I'M GOING UP ON DECK.
RIGHT BEHIND YOU!

WE CAN'T LET NOAH'S **WIFE** SEE US!

HEY, WATCH WHERE YOU'RE GOING!
OR WHAT?
OR THIS!

YAAAH!
GRRRRR!
WHOA!

OOOOOOH!
WHAM!

WE WERE NEVER HERE, RIGHT?
RIGHT.
RIGHT.

DADDY, MOMMY'S GONE TO HEAVEN.
WELL, THAT'S GONNA MAKE REPOPULATING THE EARTH A REAL DILLY OF A PICKLE.

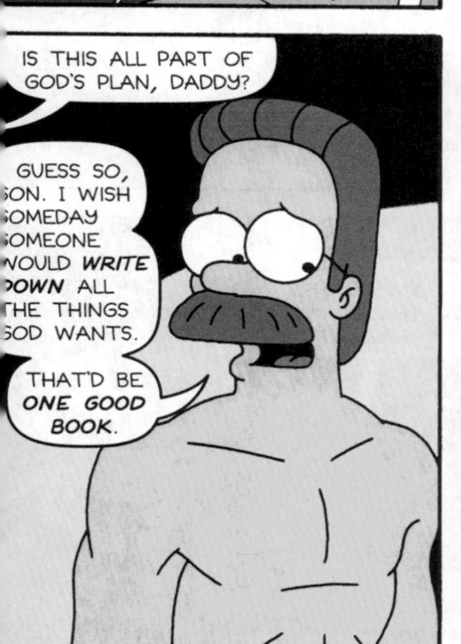
IS THIS ALL PART OF GOD'S PLAN, DADDY?
GUESS SO, SON. I WISH SOMEDAY SOMEONE WOULD WRITE DOWN ALL THE THINGS GOD WANTS.
THAT'D BE ONE GOOD BOOK.

FORTY DAYS PASS...
DADDY, DO THE ANIMALS LOOK THINNER TO YOU?
WE KEEP DOUBLING THEIR FEED. I JUST DON'T UNDERSTAND IT. IT'S LIKE ONE BIG ANIMAL IS EATING EVERYTHING.
BUT WHAT KIND OF CREATURE WOULD BE THAT SELFISH?

GASP!
HORSEFEED

WAY TO RAT US OUT!
I FIND THAT TERM *OFFENSIVE!*

I DON'T HAVE TIME TO BE MAD.
THE FOOD'S RUN OUT, AND WE NEED TO SEND THE ***PTERODACTYL*** OUT TO LOOK FOR LAND.

SOMEONE ***ATE*** ALL THE ***DINOSAURS!***
UH...YEAH, THAT'D BE ME. SORRY ABOUT THAT.

THAT DOES IT! YOU'RE GONNA MESS UP MY ARK ***NEVERMORE!***
LOOK OUT, HE'S GOT A ***RAVEN!***

TOO SLOW, NOAH! HAND ME THAT DOVE, BOY!
SPLAT!

HA! MISSED ME! YOU THROW LIKE A ***PAGAN!***
THUD!

MEANWHILE, NOAH ENDED UP HAVING TO **RENT** HIS ARK OUT FOR **SWINGING SINGLES CRUISES** JUST TO **BREAK EVEN** ON HIS ANIMAL FOOD BILLS.

ARE YOU SURE ALL THE ANIMALS ARE **GONE?** THIS SHIP **SMELLS** LIKE A ZOO DIED.

AW, SHUT UP!

THE OMEGA.

AND SO EVERYONE IN THE BIBLE LIVED **HAPPILY EVER AFTER**.
EXCEPT FOR SATAN. THE END.

YOUR BIBLE STORIES ARE **DIFFERENT** FROM THE ONES SUNDAY SCHOOL TEACHER TELLS.
SHE USES **THE KING JAMES BIBLE**. IT'S A LITTLE DIFFERENT.

THANKS, BART. THAT WAS FUN!
YEAH. THANK YOU!

AHEM!

WHAT IS IT?
THE **COLLECTION PLATE**. YOU KNOW THE CHURCH RULES. YOU GOTTA **PAY** OR ALL THE **SALVATION** DOESN'T COUNT.

BUT WE DON'T HAVE ANY **MONEY**.
ALL WE HAVE ARE OUR **BIKES**.
WELL, IF THEY'RE **MORE IMPORTANT** THAN YOUR **SOULS**...

GOD BLESS **RELIGION**.
AMEN, BROTHER!